Contents

C000183649

The writer on writing

Roy Blatchford interviews Ad de Bont

Interviewer You are a new writer to English audiences. Can you tell us a little about your own background in Holland?

Ad de Bont First of all, the theatre was not the main idea of my working life – my interest was in children. So I went to be trained as a primary school teacher; after that I trained to be a drama teacher and in the third place I went to a school for actors. I did a lot of singing and dancing in this particular school in Holland.

I think theatre, culture, literature are very important for children. I was born and lived in a very beautiful part of Holland – an old part of the country in the south – but when I was 5 years old my parents moved to a very new area, the Polders. I had a whole life of tradition and history in that old part, but when we moved to the new, modern landscape it was without tradition; the trees were only 5 years old and it was for me an empty country. I think my interest in history and culture has to do with this move of my parents.

Interviewer At what point did you discover that you had a talent for writing for the theatre?

Ad de Bont From an early age I was always interested in writing – poems, diaries, songs, anything. Later I discovered I could write for the theatre, especially when I started working for a theatre company in the late 1970s.

Interviewer And what sorts of subjects did you first start writing about?

Ad de Bont In the 1970s, Dutch theatre companies were producing plays about adults who were repressing children and children who were fighting their fathers and families – depressing social drama.

These play were sometimes improvised and sometimes scripted. When I started writing seriously I found it more important to have wider stories. So my first play – written with my colleague director – was an adaptation of Myron Levoy's novel **Alan and Naomi** about a Jewish boy and girl living in New York.

The second play I wrote, **The Particular Life of Hilletje Jans**, was about a girl in the eighteenth century in Holland. She had a wretched life and then on a particular day she decided to become a man. This was based on a study of eighty women from that period in history who 'became' men in order to go through life.

Interviewer When did you make the move from commercial theatres to theatre in schools?

Ad de Bont About twelve years ago I was asked to be the artistic director of a company (Wederzijds) working with schools – and I've done this ever since. Producing theatre within schools is much more important. For me, the traditional theatre building in Amsterdam, Paris or London is a dead building – it is a building from the nineteenth century. It stands there, nobody lives there, only five per cent of the people ever come there. The majority of people just don't go anywhere near. So it is a kind of non-place for me. And when I was acting there I always had the feeling: 'Well we have to earn our money and they have to have their social evening'. But when I first played in schools this for me was really a vibrating world: people lived there together, working on their own lives and thinking about the future of our world.

And working in schools there is no set tradition to follow. Everything is possible. You can use the classroom, the gymnasium or dining-hall in a new way as an artist. It's much more exciting to explore a space like the gym – you can sit on four sides or only one, whereas in the commercial theatre the actors are on the stage and the audience are often far away in their seats. With every new play, like **Mirad**, our company is thinking about the distance between actors and audience.

Interviewer How then did you come to write a play like **Mirad**?

Ad de Bont   As I mentioned, in the 1970s we were producing family social drama, and in the 1980s also doing a lot of artistic impro-visation. The theatre world became all very experimental, very strange for a lot of people, surrealistic even – especially for the audiences. There were good intentions but often bad theatre and bad acting.

In 1989 in Berlin the Wall fell, and then in Russia, Romania, even China, we saw incredibly important changes for people with the fall of Communism. And, interestingly, for two or three years in Holland nothing changed. The world around us changed a lot, and we just shut the curtains and we kept doing what we were doing.

And I remember about six months after the fall of the iron curtain we produced a play of mine called **The Ballad of Garuma** in East Berlin. The play is about a very poor boy in South America who has a terrible life, sniffing glue and so on, but then becomes a great football hero – a Maradonna or Pele. It's a strongly emotional play with a lot of music and celebration of freedom. In Holland we'd received a prize for the production but when we performed in East Berlin we felt this theme was really important for an audience whose lives had been terrible under Communism and now there was hope for change. That was really an electric feeling.

Interviewer   So social change in Europe was an important backcloth to **Mirad**?

Ad de Bont   Yes, but it wasn't until 1992 that our company really woke up to all this social change. We had performed a play about refugees from the war in Iran – and this idea was fascinating to me because with the fall of Communism there were a lot of people moving around Europe. It was an issue which young people could identify with. I decided I must write a play of my own about refugees – maybe from Iran, maybe Cambodia, Somalia, Bosnia. I wanted to write something about refugees but also about the way fascists in Belgium and Holland were treating them.

In January 1993 I asked one of the members of our theatre company to prepare for me all the material she could find about refugees who had recently come to Holland. She went to the Amnesty International refugee organisation and ended up with piles of articles and information that I read on holiday in about three or four weeks. I had already the idea of making the play very simple, and my first idea was to write about two people tracing a particular boy who had disappeared during a war.

Interviewer   After reading all the research material, why did you decide to write about refugees from Bosnia?

Ad de Bont   Well Cambodia and Somalia seemed to me to be so far away in young people's eyes – altogether another culture. A play about these countries might just seem rather exotic. Bosnia is so very close. The one incident I remember reading about from Amnesty International that I thought I must use was from Iran and Iraq: thousands of young people were sent to walk on minefields, to clear the air! Can you believe that?

Anyway I wanted to write the play quickly once I got started – to produce it in schools as soon as possible. I was ready in September 1993; we had four days of rehearsals and then went straight into schools.

Interviewer   And returning to your choice of characters?

Ad de Bont   First I thought of Mirad, a boy. I couldn't choose a girl because there are not many girls fleeing on their own. There are a lot more boys. In one or two years they are going to be men and dangerous. They could be fighters, soldiers – what Mirad becomes of course – so that is why many parents in times of war send their sons away.

Interviewer   But you chose not to tell the story in Part I through the boy's eyes but through the aunt and uncle?

Ad de Bont   Yes, and that was an artistic idea. I thought it would make better drama. Every person in the audience will have his or her own idea of what the boy looks like, how he thinks, how he dreams.

Of course he is the central figure. And I didn't want his mother and father talking about him because I needed them 'off-stage' to show how the war in Bosnia affected the family. I chose the uncle to be a journalist so that he could also reveal what was happening in Holland – the way refugees were being turned back by the fascists. He is someone who has seen it all before.

Interviewer   Can you tell us how you came to write Part 2?

Ad de Bont   Well of course Part 1 was the whole play to begin with. I didn't intend a Part 2. We were asked to give over a hundred performances of Part 1 in a matter of weeks – all over Holland. Two months later there were twenty theatre groups in Germany and Austria performing the play. There was a radio and a television version in Holland. And when I came to Oxford in January 1994 to see it in the big theatre with a movie star (Jeremy Irons) playing Uncle Djuka, I realised I'd written something that worked equally well with children in the classroom and with adults in the commercial theatre. I went home and had the idea that I could write about the mother and the son.

My first thought was not just to write more of the same. Rather, I wanted to explore the question, 'How do you go on living after the kind of experiences Mirad and his mother had been through?' This was for me a very important question.

And if I were to move on to write a Part 3 – I'm thinking about it – I would be curious to follow Mirad and Verica's coming to Holland to visit Djuka and Fazila. How are the Dutch treating the refugees? What do people back in Bosnia think of those who've deserted their own country? Can people survive all the hate and horror of war? Can they live with the guilt of survival when so many of their friends and family have died? Can they live at peace with themselves beyond the war? Part 3 could be for radio – just the voices of all the characters in Mirad's family, their feelings about war. For me, writing theatre is all about digging into experiences and thinking aloud about how things could be.

Interviewer   Can you talk now about the language and style of the play?

Ad de Bont   I like simple acting. If the story is strong then the acting doesn't need to be complicated. *Mirad* is not like a normal piece of drama with continuous lines — there are a lot of half-lines. I first had the idea of writing it in Dutch which was not good Dutch — full of the kind of errors made by someone whose first language is something else. I tried several pages but that didn't work. So I went for short sentences with a certain kind of rhythm, but not quite poetry — sentences without punctuation which perhaps suggest that it's not realistic. For the same reason of simplicity I didn't include any stage directions.

I also like to build a play not necessarily in a chronological order. My play *Garuma* has a whole series of flashbacks and flash-forwards. So *Mirad* was built in a similar way — quite a complex structure in fact but one which seems simple on the stage. And I think reading plays is sometimes quite difficult but I hope this one is quite easy to read.

Interviewer   When you read or see *Mirad*, what for you are the most powerful moments?

Ad de Bont   In Part 1 it would have to be the story about the father in the minefield. And in the second part it is when the mother is going to have the child (following her rape) and she has the idea of killing the child and then killing herself.

Interviewer   You have a lot of experience of working with young people. These two moments you've chosen are violent — do you think that they are suitable for a young audience?

Ad de Bont   I was trained as a teacher. I believe education has to prepare children for life that is real, and too often I believe over the past fifty years in Western Europe we have just prepared children for a 'youthland' that adults *think* is real. And it isn't. Terrible things happen in this world. I mean as a girl you can be raped, even if you are just 11 and live in a village. If there is war, you know almost for sure you might be raped – you are very glad when you are not. Nobody says in war: 'I won't shoot your father because you are too young'. What I can say is that children who have seen *Mirad* say to me that now they understand how people at war can be so terrible to each other. *Mirad* is both theatre and reality.

Interviewer   Do you have hopes that a play like *Mirad* – alongside other plays, books and television documentaries – can ever help end war?

Ad de Bont   The war in Bosnia might end, yes. But it won't be because of this play. What I've written might just help people change the way they think about war and refugees.

Interviewer   Finally, has something been said to you by a child in a school which made you feel the play was really worth writing?

Ad de Bont   It was not a child. It was a grown man who saw it in a theatre in Amsterdam and he said: 'This was really my story and I am surprised as I couldn't imagine that a Dutchman could write it'. He was a Bosnian.

Introduction

Bosnia is one of Europe's oldest countries. It is a land with a remarkable political and cultural history, in which the great religions and great powers of European history have combined and overlapped. In the Middle Ages it formed a powerful independent kingdom. Later it was occupied by Turks and Austrians, and for much of the twentieth century it has been part of the country of Yugoslavia. Close study of a map of Europe shows its critical geographical position on the Adriatic Sea's eastern shores.

In November 1989 the fall of the Berlin Wall marked a turning point in the twentieth-century history of Europe, with the countries of Eastern Europe gradually emerging from the dominance of Communism and the USSR. In April 1992 the people of Bosnia voted for independence from their neighbouring states of Serbia and Croatia, and from Yugoslavia. Thus the seeds of war were sown.

Historians, politicians and the Bosnian people themselves are deeply divided about the exact causes of their internal war. It is a multi-ethnic state: approximately 44 per cent of the population is Muslim, 17 per cent Croatian Catholic, and 31 per cent Serbian Christian Orthodox. There are also small minorities of Jews, Albanians, Gypsies and others. Clearly differences exist. What *is* true is that Muslims, Croats and Serbians within Bosnia turned upon each other – assisted by various external forces – with a hatred and ferocity that has few parallels in the twentieth century.

During the 1990s there have been many tens of thousands killed, more than two million people expelled from their homes, unknown thousands of girls and women raped, villages and towns burnt and devastated, and several hundred mosques and churches deliberately blown up.

Much of this war has been beamed into homes around the world on a daily basis through news bulletins featuring frightened children in the sniper-ridden streets of Sarajevo, the capital city. Young generations of radio listeners and television viewers have been introduced to a vocabulary of 'ethnic cleansing', 'no-fly-zones', 'safe havens', and 'legit-imising genocide'. This macabre, live soap-opera has – perhaps courtesy of the all-powerful, global television companies – inevitably drawn in United Nations peace-keeping forces and all the political debate that accompanies the UN's involvement anywhere in the world.

Beyond the frontiers of the old Yugoslavia, the war in Bosnia has of course thrown up the great and inescapable by-product of war: thousands of refugees have left their shattered homelands to seek a new (perhaps temporary) life in Italy, Germany, Hungary, Holland, Romania, England.

Mirad, A Boy from Bosnia is a play set amidst the horrors of the Bosnian conflicts and which also skilfully takes its audience into the hearts and minds of those refugees of war. Playwright Ad de Bont explains on pages v–xi how he came to write the drama. He is not concerned with the fruitless question: 'Who is to blame?' Rather he wants simply to ask human beings: 'Why go to war with one another?'

Shakespeare's play **Romeo and Juliet** opens with the lines:

Two households, both alike in dignity,
In fair Verona where we lay our scene,
From ancient grudge break to new mutiny,
Where civil blood makes civil hands unclean.

Mirad transfers these lines from sixteenth-century Italy to twentieth-century Bosnia, Croatia and Serbia, reminding us powerfully that human beings feel nothing more deeply than their sense of family, ethnic and religious belonging.

Reading log

One of the most effective ways of keeping track of your reading is to keep a log book. This can be any exercise book or folder that you have to hand, but make sure you reserve it exclusively for reflecting on your reading.

As you read the play, consider the following:

- Draw maps, sketches and doodles to help hold certain places and characters in your mind.
- Are there any incidents in the plot which strike you as significant, unusual, confusing, unconvincing, or unexpected?
- Do characters' words or behaviour seem especially important or memorable? Are any particular words or phrases associated with particular characters?
- How does your response to certain characters develop or alter as you read?
- Are there any patterns you notice in the way the play is structured? Do any key ideas or phrases recur?
- What themes do you notice? Which of these seem the most and least important?
- How does the author use language throughout the play? Is vocabulary complex or simple, or does it vary according to character and situation?
- Reflect upon your own reading process: at which points do you read most quickly? When do you slow down? Why is this?
- Finally, as you look back on the play, which moments stick in your mind?

Mirad, A Boy from Bosnia

Part 1

With thanks to Jeremy Irons and Sinead Cusack for bringing this translation alive

Characters

FAZILA BALIC, *Mirad's aunt*

DJUKA BALIC, *Mirad's uncle*

Prologue

FAZILA:
Sorry.
Sorry that we are here.
That we take your time.

DJUKA:
Sorry.

FAZILA:
Sorry that we breathe in your air.

DJUKA:
That we walk on your ground.

FAZILA:
That we stand in your view.

DJUKA:
Sorry.

FAZILA:
Yes sorry.

DJUKA:
Sorry that we look like we do.

FAZILA:
So ugly.

DJUKA:
No, not ugly.
Different.

FAZILA:
Ugly.
We are ugly people.

DJUKA:
  Maybe I am, but you are not.

FAZILA:
  Ugly people in ugly clothes.

DJUKA:
  You are not ugly.

FAZILA:
  Yes I am.
  For them I am.

DJUKA:
  For me you are as beautiful as ...

FAZILA:
  Djuka please.

DJUKA:
  Sorry.

FAZILA:
  Sorry that we disturb your rest.

DJUKA:
  As if you don't do enough for us already.

FAZILA:
  Sorry that we are not grateful and happy.

DJUKA:
  Not grateful enough.

FAZILA:
  And that our name is not David or Catherine or
  Peter or Mary.

DJUKA:
  But Djuka.

FAZILA:
  And Fazila.

DJUKA:

Sorry that we live in a normal house,
one of your houses.

FAZILA:

That we didn't say no.

DJUKA:

That we sit in your trains and buses.

FAZILA:

And on your benches in the sun.

DJUKA:

And sorry that we brought nothing.

FAZILA:

No filled vine-leaves or other delicacies.

DJUKA:

Or a series of slides.

FAZILA:

Or hand-painted puppets.

DJUKA:

The only thing we have is a story.

FAZILA:

Not even a happy story.

DJUKA:

But it is ours.
We don't have another.
Ours and our nephew's, Mirad.

Scene 1

FAZILA:
Name...
Your name.
Ihre Name.
Votre nom.
Il suo nome.

DJUKA:
I speak four languages
but I didn't understand what he wanted.

FAZILA:
Where do you come from,
woher kommen Sie,
d'où êtes vous?

DJUKA:
Serbo-croatian, Russian, French and German,
but my head was suddenly completely empty.

FAZILA:
Why are you looking at me, son?
Your passport please,
votre passeport.

DJUKA:
I only saw that mouth,
that moving mouth,
that mouth full of rat-teeth
with which Zigic,
the worst of all,

in a night,
one of those terrifying nights,
with one of my friends...

FAZILA:
Jesus Christ
again such an illiterate.
Country. Pays.
Turkey, Yugoslavia . . .?

DJUKA:
No no, Bosnia-Herzegovina.

FAZILA:
O, now you can speak.
Refugee,
Flüchtling,
réfugié.
That way,
cette direction.

DJUKA:
But I am no refugee,
for I did not flee.
I have been blown away
like a leaf from a tree.
In our country a terrible wind has risen,
a wind full of fire and rape.
And one day,
a day I don't remember,
a day I don't dare to remember,
I was blown away.
Who would think of fleeing
without saying goodbye to his own house,
his own village or city,
his own country,

who would think of leaving his own family?
And then arrive some place where you are not
welcome.
Refugees are never welcome.
Nowhere.
Everybody knows that.
History has proven it so often.
Why would you flee then?
Why a slow death in a strange country
if you can die on the threshold
of your own house?
Refugees don't exist.
Only blown away people exist,
people blown by the wind
all over the world.

Scene 2

FAZILA:

Nunspeet,* 31st August 1992.

Dear Aunt Fazila,

Are you still alive?

If you are dead already they can put this letter upon your grave.

A week ago I arrived in Holland.

I don't know if I have to feel happy or sad.

In Bosnia I was always afraid.

Now I am always alone.

The people here are nice but they seem to be behind a thick glass wall.

I am afraid of the future because I don't have any.

At night it's the worst,

then I dream of everything that happened.

Especially about Daddy and about little Djelana.

Did Uncle Djuka get the blanket?

And did you hear from Grandmother and Grandfather Balic?

Do they still live in Foca or have they been chased away?

Dutch people are strange.

If you tell somebody you come from Bosnia they look so pitiful at you

but two minutes later they laugh and eat ice-cream.

Now I am in my room in Valentijn,

that is a house for children who fled on their own.

*little village in Holland

In the other bed a boy of thirteen from Somalia is
sleeping
but I cannot speak with him.
Abdul is his name.
Sometimes he sits for hours on his bed.
Staring.
When you look at him he begins to
scream or to cry furiously.
So I don't look.
One time I dreamed about mama.
That she came home from the market and went into
the kitchen.
As if everything was normal.
Do you think that still can happen?
Rostam,
a Kurdish boy who lives here too,
he says it can.
In a war everything can happen he says.
Even a miracle.

Scene 3

DJUKA:
We heard about it a week later.
My brother,
Mirad's father,
said that he did not realise in the beginning.
That he was waiting for days.
At home.
Sitting at the table.
Very silent
without feeling anything,
without thinking anything.
He was waiting only waiting until she'd come back.
But she didn't come back.
And after three days he had tried to phone me
but the connection with Sarajevo was blocked
already.

FAZILA:
It happened on 8th April 1992.

DJUKA:
On the first day of the war.
I had been afraid of that all the time
because my brother lived in Foca.
In the south of Bosnia.
Not far from the border with Serbia and
Montenegro.
So if war was going to break out it would be there.

FAZILA:

The day before,
7th April,
Mirad had his birthday.
Thirteen.

DJUKA:

And the whole country put out the flag.

FAZILA:

Not for Mirad but for the Americans and all the
countries of Europe that acknowledged us.
Exactly on that day.

DJUKA:

That was very important for us,
because that made our country really independent.

FAZILA:

Mirad had asked for peace for his birthday.
Imagine, a boy of thirteen who asks for peace as a
birthday present.

DJUKA:

He was a special boy.

FAZILA:

He is a special boy.
He is not yet dead.

DJUKA:

Of course not,
that is not what I meant.
Mirad is a special boy because he thinks about everything.

FAZILA:

You have to
when you are from Bosnia

and a Muslim.

DJUKA:

But who does?

Who is thinking in our country?

Who can think?

During Communism we learned to obey,

not to think,

not to choose for ourselves.

If we had learned,

we would not live in a hell like this.

FAZILA:

When Mirad used to come to stay with us in
Sarajevo,

we often talked politics.

The war between Serbia and Croatia was going on by
then,

but in Bosnia it was still quiet.

I remember he asked,

'But the Croats and the Serbians got along very well
in the old days.

Why do they fight?'

DJUKA:

What can you say?

I wish I knew why.

I wish anybody knew why.

We lived eighteen years in Sarajevo

and all those years nobody cared

whether you were Muslim, Serb or Croat.

We just lived together.

Our neighbours were Croats,

nice people,

and our best friends were Serbs.

About your colleagues you didn't even know,

nobody cared,
and suddenly everybody starts to murder each other.
Not really suddenly,
for years you could see it coming,
because we were poisoned,
poisoned slowly but surely,
all of us,
and infected with the virus of hate.
The war did not break out last year,
it already started ten years ago.
In the papers, on the radio and on television.
For how many years didn't the Serbian
media shout that we are Muslim beasts?
And you Croats too.

FAZILA:

Don't call me 'you Croats'.

DJUKA:

Not human beings,
but beasts that strangle newborn babies,
rape Serbian women,
sew them up
and let dogs tear their men to pieces.
You saw it yourself on the Serbian television,
forty-one dead children.
Filmed with care and a whining voice telling that this
is the work of Croatian soldiers,
when in fact they were Serbian.

FAZILA:

Don't call me 'you'.
I am one of yours.

DJUKA:

Of course you are,

but you are also Croatian.
Your whole family lives in Croatia.
You are also one of them,
the occupiers of my country,
of our country
Bosnia-Herzegovina
which, incidentally, is exactly the same.
There every Croatian is seen as a bodysnatcher
and every Serb as a torturer.
Only Muslims seem to be human,
the rest are rubbish,
ready for the cemetery.
Maybe it's right that Bosnia is cleared out.

FAZILA:

Don't talk like that.
Not to me
and not to them.
What's the use if you don't have hope?
Do you think that they've come here to hear that?

DJUKA:

Do you have hope?

FAZILA:

Yes, you bastard,
I do have a glimmer of hope,
and I won't let you take it away.
I'd rather jump in front of a train.

DJUKA:

And that's hope?

FAZILA:

I have hope that what's happened to us will not
happen to them.

DJUKA:

Sorry.

13

You are right.
Where were we?
On Mirad's birthday.
Come on,
come on, tell us.

FAZILA:
What?

DJUKA:
How he celebrated his birthday.
Mirad.
His thirteenth birthday.
Last year.

FAZILA:
You tell it.

DJUKA:
No, you.
Please.

FAZILA:
Okay.
Mirad had asked for peace as a birthday present.
Peace for everybody in Bosnia.
Not only for the Muslims.
But also for the Croats and
the Serbs who live there.
And that's why he gave a party.
He invited four Croatian, four Serbian
and three Muslim friends.
The twelve of them moved through the streets like a
demonstration.
Singing, dancing, arms round each other.

DJUKA:
And that evening

14

in Foca eleven boys –
four Croatian,
four Serbian
and three Muslim –
were thrashed by their fathers
until blood ran down their backs.

FAZILA:
And the next morning, 8th April 1992,
around nine o'clock
the first bands of Serbs appeared in the city.
Heavily armed.
With black bands around their heads.
The liberators,
that's how they called themselves later.
They drove directly to the market place
because there was a market,
and they started to shoot at random.
Everybody fled in panic.
People who stumbled were trampled over,
driven over by the Serbs
or taken away.
In the houses of some Muslims
they threw firebombs.
Then they disappeared.
The liberators.
My brother-in-law told me
fifteen people died that first day,
fifty-four were wounded
and four people missing –
all four, young women.
And one of them
was Mirad's mother.

Scene 4

DJUKA:
Sarajevo, 14th January 1992.
Today I,
Mirad Balic from Foca,
start a diary
because a new life begins.
I am staying a couple of days
with my Uncle Djuka and my Aunt Fazila
here in Sarajevo.
We celebrated the orthodox New Year with Serbian
friends of Uncle Djuka.
Until yesterday I still felt a schoolboy.
And I was.
But since the speech of Nenad Pejic on Sarajevo tele-
vision I feel quite different.
As if I'm awake for the first time.
I never understood anything about politics,
just like my friends.
But suddenly, last night,
I understood it's about ourselves.
About all ordinary people.
Nenad Pejic said that the political parties of Bosnia
are leading us into a civil war
by setting us against each other
and he asked the public

if they agreed that we need peace and cooperation,
peace and cooperation.
If they agreed they were to switch off
all the lights in their house.
We immediately switched off everything.
In the living room,
in the kitchen,
in the hall,
everywhere.
Only the television was on.
Then we went on to the balcony.
We were curious to see whether many
people would switch off their lights.
And as we stood there,
looking out over Sarajevo,
we saw how the whole city became dark within five
minutes.
Sarajevo looked like a Christmas tree
with all the lights going out one by one.
Only the streetlights were on
and everybody stood on their balcony looking into
the darkness.
So nobody wants war.
I've been thinking about something all night,
That my mother is not Muslim, but Serbian.
I never realised that.
What's the difference?
Aunt Fazila is Croatian.
Daddy and Uncle Djuka have mixed marriages,
so we are a mixed family.
Is that dangerous in the war?
Maybe it would have been better not to wake up.

Scene 5

FAZILA:
To the wall.
Turn.
Arms on your back.
Head against the wall.
Beat your head against the wall.
Again.
Harder.
Harder I say.
Do you need any help?
Enough.
On your knees.
Lick my shoes.
Cleaner.
More.
Up on your feet.
Straighten up.
Straighten your arms out.
Forward.
Spread your fingers.
Now you can choose.
Either I'll break them one by one
or I'll bite one off.
Only one.
The one you hold your pen with.

With my teeth.
What do you say?
Well,
what do you choose?
Tell me.
Or shall I ask you some questions
and you give the right answers?
Because you're not at all the unimportant guy
you want us to believe you are.
We took that little nephew of yours, Mirad,
we weren't too cruel,
he is a child,
I don't think more than a few broken ribs,
and guess what?
You are Djuka Balic,
freelance journalist in Sarajevo.
Isn't that a surprise?
Because you've been on our list a long time.
Your filthy Muslim articles.
Enough talking.
Your turn.
Tell us about Sarajevo in wartime.
Did you have any water, electricity, petrol?
Did you have any food?
How much ammunition did you have
and where do you store it?
Tell me.

DJUKA:
I have nothing to say.

FAZILA:
You are a journalist, aren't you?
Then it is your profession to be curious.

DJUKA:

    I write about other things.

FAZILA:

    Of course.

    Of course you write about other things.

    But sometimes you see something,

    you hear something,

    something interesting,

    you know what I mean.

DJUKA:

    I have nothing to say.

FAZILA:

    Really?

DJUKA:

    No.

FAZILA:

    So, you have nothing to tell us.

DJUKA:

    No, I am sorry.

FAZILA:

    That is a pity,

    a real pity.

    Then we go on.

    Arms forward.

    Spread your fingers.

    Spread your fingers!

    What do you prefer?

    Break or bite?

DJUKA:

    You are not allowed to do this.

FAZILA:
   Who says so?

DJUKA:
   There is a convention between your president and
   ours
   that forbids any violation of human rights.

FAZILA:
   Since when?

DJUKA:
   Since the 22nd of May.

FAZILA:
   Listen, son,
   there's a war on
   and with your so-called intellectual human rights
   I wipe my ass.

DJUKA:
   After the war you can be punished for this.

FAZILA:
   Who would be a witness?

DJUKA:
   The survivors.

FAZILA:
   Will there be any?

DJUKA:
   There are always survivors.

FAZILA:
   You think so?

DJUKA:
   No matter how many you kill,
   every killer gets tired, eventually.

FAZILA:
Not every one.
We have one who never gets tired,
he kills for pleasure.
Zigic,
you know,
the fat one
who two weeks ago, to honour Holy Peter,
set fire to a pile of rubber tyres
and threw a man on the fire.
Alive.
You heard about that.
You know what?
I'll send you to him.
Why should I dirty my hands?
Or would you like to tell me something?

DJUKA:
I have nothing to say.

FAZILA:
Be sensible.

DJUKA:
No, really.

FAZILA:
Really?
It's a pity,
a great pity.
Zigic is going to think it is a pity too.

DJUKA:
Zigic ...
Zigic ...

Scene 6

FAZILA:
Nunspeet, 28th September 1992.
Dear, dear Aunt Fazila,
I was very glad to get your letter,
almost as glad as the moment they let me out of the camp.
At last I have a family.
These last weeks I asked every day whether there was any post for me,
but there never was.
So I thought they're all dead.
It's fantastic that you are alive
and maybe Uncle Djuka,
because that blanket will make a difference.
I like it better here every day.
In Valentijn I mean.
Every day we learn Dutch for six hours,
so I can say something,
and Abdul and I can speak with each other now.
A little bit.
With hands and feet.
Every day we watch the news programmes on television.
What we cannot see they tape for us
because Dutch people do a lot about civil wars.
Not only in Bosnia but also in Somalia
and Cambodia and so on.

Everybody hopes to see a familiar face on the telly.
Two times I thought I saw you in Sarajevo,
but there was too much smoke
and it was too short.
Yesterday I asked for asylum.
Somebody in the house helped me with it.
But I am allowed to fill in the form myself
because I am over twelve.
They asked all kinds of questions
because not all refugees are allowed to stay in
Holland.
They asked if my father and mother were still alive.
I said my father not
but my mother maybe yes.
And then they asked me to tell what happened to my
father,
but I could not.
My throat closed up.
So I said I'll write it down.
And that was okay.
They did not ask about little Djelana.
That was lucky.
I would have cried.

Scene 7

DJUKA:

Do you realise we are not even Muslims?
Muslims are people who believe in Allah.
I don't believe in Allah.
I don't believe at all.
My brother didn't believe either.
Or my father.
Or my mother.
And none of the rest of the family.
And it was the same with my Muslim friends.
Who did believe after all?
In fact, I believe that most Bosnian Muslims
are atheists.
They're people who don't have a God.
This isn't surprising
because under Communism every religion
was considered an illness
that should be cured as soon as possible.
But why do they call us Muslims?
It was Tito's idea,
Our great leader,
the father of old Yugoslavia.
He worked out that everybody in our country
who was not Serbian or Croatian had to be called
Muslim,
so the three of them could form a balance:
Serbs, Croats and Muslims.

So it was easier for him to keep power.
You see how that ended up.
We are murdered for something we are not.
God's ways are impenetrable
and humanity is heartless –
because who does anything?
After the Second World War
in 1948 they founded the UN
the United Nations
so that a thing like mass murder of the Jews
could never happen again.
Now the UN is a flourishing organisation,
an honourable institution,
the only thing is
that it doesn't do the thing
they founded it for:
prevention of mass murder.

Scene 8

FAZILA:

The fight for Foca took three months.
In the first weeks Mirad's father
spent all his time looking for his wife.
About the missing women there were
all sorts of rumours.
That they were in a camp in Serbia,
that they had to cook for the soldiers
but also that they were used as hostages
or as human shields.
At that time nobody knew about the camps
where women were raped.

DJUKA:

My brother looked everywhere,
afraid of nothing.
When he heard that he could buy her
freedom maybe,
he walked up to a Serbian post in the mountains
and he asked how much money they wanted.
They only laughed at him
and he came back beaten up.

FAZILA:

Then came that horrible May 20th.
It was around noon,
Mirad was in the kitchen
because since his mother was away
he did the cooking.

Djelana was playing outside in the street
with some of the kids next door.
Mirad told her to stay close to the house
but they had been running after a young kitten.
So when the shooting started
she was a couple of hundred metres
away from the house.

DJUKA:

Immediately he heard the first explosion,
Mirad ran outside.
'Djelana inside!'
he cried. 'Into the cellar.'
But she wasn't there.
He looked up the street
and saw her far away.
'Djelana, come quick!'
he cried
and started to run to her.

FAZILA:

Djelana's friends were brought inside
by their mothers, aunts, brothers and sisters.
Mirad ran as quick as he could,
he was very close,
another thirty metres.
Suddenly he saw in a second something coming
towards Djelana,
a metre in front of her
it fell on the ground
and exploded.
Djelana looked at Mirad;
she opened her mouth
as if she wanted to say something

and grasped her belly with both hands.

DJUKA:
  Mirad stood still
  and looked at his sister.
  Under her hands the colour of her dress
  changed slowly to red.
  'Djelana',
  he said,
  'are you hurt?
  Is it bad?
  Shall I have a look?'

FAZILA:
  But Djelana said nothing.
  She kept looking at him
  and slowly fell to the ground.

DJUKA:
  Mirad ran to catch her
  but before he reached her
  she sank to the ground.

FAZILA:
  'Djelana.
  Djelana,
  are you still alive?'
  asked Mirad.
  But she could not answer.
  A moment later her tongue was thick
  and it was as if she held her breath.
  Then she gave a big sigh
  and looked at Mirad
  with strange
  dead eyes.

DJUKA:
    Then Mirad saw
    that her tummy
    was full of shrapnel
    and while the mortars fell around them
    he put his face
    to his sister's
    and cried.
    Djelana.
    Djelana.

Scene 9

FAZILA:

Can he do it?
How can he start again?

DJUKA:

I don't know.
But he has to.
We all have to.

FAZILA:

They killed his father,
took away his mother
and his sister died in his arms.
What else can he do but feel hate?
Hate, hate and more hate.

DJUKA:

Start all over again.
like all people
after every war.

FAZILA:

How can he start again,
he only wants revenge.

DJUKA:

Of course.
Everybody wants revenge.
You too.
I want nothing more than to strangle Zigic
with my own hands.
But what is the use?

FAZILA:

How can he do it?

DJUKA:

No idea,
but it must be done.
And us, we also have to start all over again.
The last ten years we have learned how to hate.
The next ten years we'll have to learn how to live
together.
That is all we can do.

FAZILA:

Poor Mirad.

DJUKA:

Don't pity him,
Mirad will be all right.
He is young,
he has his whole life before him.
I'm more afraid for us.
How will we manage?
Can we start again?
Maybe we are bound to this hatred for ever.
Wherever we are?
Mmm?

FAZILA:

I don't know.
I really don't know.

DJUKA:

If we cannot we put an end to it.

FAZILA:

End to what?

DJUKA:

Life.

FAZILA:

Never.

DJUKA:

Why not?

What can the world do with two unhappy people,
full of hate?

FAZILA:

I won't leave Mirad behind.

We're the only thing he still has.

So we have to keep going,

Whatever the cost.

DJUKA:

You are a saint.

My own saint.

I love you.

FAZILA:

Djuka, please.

DJUKA:

Sorry.

Sorry.

Scene 10

FAZILA:
>   After the defeat of Foca,
>   three months after the start of the war,
>   and after the death of his father,
>   Mirad fled to us,
>   to Sarajevo.

DJUKA:
>   That was the beginning of July 1992.
>   Sarajevo was under siege.
>   Every day we were shot at and everywhere snipers
>   were hiding,
>   but Mirad didn't know where else to go.

FAZILA:
>   He could not go to his grandparents, the Balics.
>   They were in jail,
>   in the old town hall of Foca.

DJUKA:
>   He didn't dare to go to his grandmother and grand-
>   father Kovac,
>   for they lived in Bistrica,
>   in Serbia.

FAZILA:
>   Aunt Vineta and Uncle Stipo
>   had fled to Sweden in May.

DJUKA:
>   Aunt Marika and Uncle Bozo had been chased out
>   of the city

with seven thousand other Muslims.

FAZILA:
And Aunt Liljana and Uncle Milos
were out of the question
because Uncle Milos,
the brother of his mother,
was an officer in the Serbian army.

DJUKA:
So to Sarajevo.

FAZILA:
Foca to Sarajevo is ninety kilometres.

DJUKA:
And it took Mirad four days.
Or rather four nights because he
slept during the day
and walked through the night.

FAZILA:
Along the road
hundreds of houses were burnt out,
everywhere bodies,
crippled, half wasted, swollen bodies.

DJUKA:
One night,
just when he wanted to start walking again,
Mirad saw how two soldiers drove their bayonets into
some swollen bodies.

FAZILA:
He almost vomited.

DJUKA:
But later, in Sarajevo,
when he saw all the bodies in the streets,

35

he understood the soldiers did it
because the bodies could explode
and spread all kinds of diseases.

FAZILA:

How he passed all those Serbian control posts,
alone without identity papers,
I have no idea.
But one night
just before curfew,
he arrived at our door.

DJUKA:

He looked like a ghost.
More than skinny,
dead pale,
totally filthy,
and his whole body trembling.

FAZILA:

We were shocked.
We hadn't seen him since January
and at the time he was a healthy boy.

DJUKA:

He was shocked to see us.
We looked like idiots after two months in the cellars.

FAZILA:

Then he told us everything.
We were speechless.

DJUKA:

First we tried to smarten him up,
as far as possible of course,
for without water, without food and without
medicine you cannot do much.

FAZILA:

Don't forget all those shells and mortars
day and night,
it was enough to drive you crazy.
So one thing was clear:
Mirad had to get out of Sarajevo
as soon as possible.

DJUKA:

So did we but we thought
we can't just up and leave everything
just like that.

FAZILA:

We shouldn't have been that stupid,
maybe we could have got away in time.

DJUKA:

If we had fled earlier
Mirad would have arrived at an empty house.

FAZILA:

No, the three of us,
we should've all tried to get out of
this damned city, all three.

DJUKA:

Then they would have caught all three of us.
That way, at least you would have escaped.

FAZILA:

Well, whatever,
we agreed Mirad had to leave the city,
but where to?

DJUKA:

Suddenly I thought of Serbian friends in Krupac,
just outside Sarajevo in the mountains.

Very nice people with a son about Mirad's age.
They would take him in.

FAZILA:
Djuka would go with him,
we thought it irresponsible to let
him go on his own
with all those snipers in a strange city.

DJUKA:
And I knew how you could get out of the city.
At least I thought I knew.

FAZILA:
It was the evening of the 25th of July.
I remember quite well,
it had been so hot that day,
but rather quiet.
No shooting I mean.
I had been with a friend
that afternoon,
Evica,
a Serbian woman,
very nice.
We drank Turkish coffee.
When I told her our plans
she said, 'Wait'
and she put her cup upside down
on the saucer.
The coffee grounds dribbled down
and she stared at them.
I said, 'Come on, Evica,
you don't believe in that?'
'It's war,' she said,
'and my grandmother always told me:

"if this can help you, why not?'"
After that she concentrated on the cup
and after she'd shaken it again
she said,
'Don't let them go.
Not tonight.
Maybe tomorrow or the day after,
but not tonight.'

DJUKA:
We should have listened to her.

FAZILA:
That's what I said
but you had to leave.

DJUKA:
I couldn't keep beating my head against a brick wall.

FAZILA:
Why are you always so stubborn?

DJUKA:
Yes, why?
Who knows?

FAZILA:
So they left.
In the evening around eleven o'clock.

DJUKA:
It went very well,
I knew the way we had to go
and it was all just as I expected
until we got to one of the last control posts.
'It should be behind the water tower,'
they said,
but it had been moved in front.

Suddenly we stood in plain view
of some Serbian soldiers,
fully armed
and we couldn't get away.
If we ran they would shoot us.
So I said to Mirad:
'Quiet.
Stay quiet,
maybe we have a chance.'
And we strolled to the post
as if we were going to the zoo.
I don't think
there are many people
who have walked so quietly into a trap
as we did.
And then it started,
that bloody circus of questions,
threats, sufferings and tortures.
The first camp,
Keraterm,
was the worst,
so I was very glad that Mirad was let out after two weeks
because he would never have come
through it alive.
That he would be allowed to go to Holland
directly after leaving that camp
I didn't know then.
Of course.
That was a chance you could only dream about.

Scene 11

FAZILA:
Nunspeet, 29th September 1992.
Dear Sir,
I am Mirad Balic from Foca.
You asked me to write down what happened
to my father.
That's what I am going to do for you now.
Please excuse my handwriting
because I tremble a bit sometimes.
That is because of the war.
In school in Foca I didn't tremble at all.
The last time I saw my father
was on the 6th July.
After that nobody saw him
because he didn't exist any more.
That day we were taken out of the prison
that we had been put in some days before.
When the Serbs took Foca,
we didn't get anything to eat,
only some water
and we were beaten up many times.
I knew one of the guards,
he used to be our neighbour.
The second night
some of the men were taken outside
and beaten terribly with sticks,
gunbutts and chains.

My father was one of them
and he told me
that our neighbour had beaten him with an iron
stick on the soles of his feet.
The man used to be friendly and polite.
My father couldn't understand,
nor could I.

DJUKA:
That day about fifty men and boys
were taken for a 'technical expedition',
they said.
We walked out of the city
and reached a field full of clover.
We had to stand next to each other
and join hands.
Then the Serbs told us to walk slowly
into the clover-field.
Suddenly one of the prisoners,
Mister Poljac,
the father of my friend Ante,
cried out: 'Don't do it, don't go,
the field is heavily mined.'
As he cried out he was shot.
Nobody was allowed to pick him up.
Not even Ante.
Then we walked into the mined field.
Never before had I been so afraid,
not all my life,
because every step could be your last.
But I was most afraid for my father,
that he would step on a mine.
My father didn't walk beside me,

that was forbidden,
he was at a distance at the end of the line.
The line was a bit curved
so that I could see him.
I was glad about that.
And then it happened.
I looked at the ground
for I saw something small sticking out
and I was afraid it was a mine.
Then I heard a loud explosion.
Somebody had stepped on a mine.
I looked to my father
but all I saw
was a cloud of mud and blood.
I shouted 'Daddy'
and I ran without thinking
right over the field
to the spot where my father had walked.
Then, one right after another
there were more explosions.
Everybody wanted to run away in panic
but the Serbs were still behind us
and started to shoot with machine guns.
All over the field were dead bodies and wounded
people.
Some men were crying horribly
because their arms or legs had been blown off by a
mine.
So the Serbs left the engine of their tank running,
very loudly,
so that nobody could hear the
shooting and crying any more.

They kept shooting until nobody walked
over the clover-field any more.
Then they left.
I was lying very still all the time,
as if I was shot at the first firing.
But also because I'd found the hand of my father,
the hand with the little finger
without a nail.
So I knew he was dead.
I felt dead too.
All the shooting and crying didn't bother me any
more.
I don't know how long I lay in the clover-field
holding my father's hand in my hand.
When it grew dark I stood up.
I buried my father's hand
and started walking.
Away from Foca.
Later I thought I could go to Sarajevo,
to Uncle Djuka and Aunt Fazila.

Scene 12

FAZILA:
> There's not much more to tell.
> My husband was in three different camps.
> What he went through there is impossible to describe.
> He does not want to talk about it,
> it is too painful for him.
> I was in Sarajevo all the time
> so I knew nothing.
> Not where he was.
> Not whether he was alive,
> not even what happened.
> Nothing. Horrible.
> It was only when Mirad arrived in Holland
> that I heard via the International Red Cross
> that they were caught that night together.
> I decided to wait for my husband in Sarajevo
> so that he could find me
> if he was set free.
> Finally, after a terrible winter,
> they let him out on 4th April 1993.
> In exchange for Serbian prisoners of war.
> They brought them on buses to a reception centre in Croatia.
> There was an official letter for him
> saying that he was invited to come to Holland as a selected refugee.

As his wife and Mirad's aunt, that was also valid for
me.
So I travelled in a Red Cross convoy
from Sarajevo to Karlovac.

DJUKA:

There I saw Fazila for the first time in nine months.

Scene 13

FAZILA:
Djuka.
Djuka it is you.

DJUKA:
Yes.
Yes it's me.
And you.
It's you Fazila.

FAZILA:
Yes I am Fazila.
Your own Fazila.

DJUKA:
How do I look?

FAZILA:
Good.
Good.
Not so bad.
And me?

DJUKA:
You too.
No, I mean no.
You don't look well.
You don't look well at all.
I can almost see through you.

FAZILA:
O Djuka

I am so glad you are alive.

DJUKA:

And you.

Let me hold you.

Do I stink?

FAZILA:

Yes you stink,

the smell is horrible,

like carbolic soap.

DJUKA:

Did you dye your hair?

FAZILA:

No.

It came by itself.

In one night.

Does it suit me?

DJUKA:

No it doesn't.

Hold me.

Hold me close.

Am I skinny?

FAZILA:

Yes.

Yes you are skinny,

so skinny.

I can feel your bones.

You look like a skeleton.

DJUKA:

Do you mind?

FAZILA:

No.

Yes.
For you.
What did they do to you?

DJUKA:

Ssh.
Don't talk about it.
I have never been so happy.

FAZILA:

When?

DJUKA:

Like now.
Where are your breasts?

FAZILA:

They went flat in Sarajevo
while you were gone.
Do you mind?

DJUKA:

No.
Yes.
For you.
And a little bit for me.

FAZILA:

Shall I get new ones?

DJUKA:

Don't.
What does an old man like me
want to do with new breasts?

FAZILA:

Are you tired?

DJUKA:

Yes.

Very tired.
I would like to sleep and never wake up again.

FAZILA:

Never?

DJUKA:

And you?

FAZILA:

I am so glad you're alive.

DJUKA:

But for yourself.

FAZILA:

O Djuka
what happened to you?

DJUKA:

Ssh.
You are here now.
Just like before.

FAZILA:

Do you want to go to Holland?

DJUKA:

They say it rains there all the time.
And you?

FAZILA:

They say it's a hospitable country.

DJUKA:

Do you believe that?

FAZILA:

It is our only chance.

DJUKA:

Yes.

It is our only chance
so we should go.

FAZILA:
Do you think it can be like before?

DJUKA:
What?

FAZILA:
Between us.

DJUKA:
I think so.
But different.
Everything is different.

FAZILA:
Yes.
Everything is different for ever.

Scene 14

DJUKA:
>When we arrived in Holland
>we immediately went to see the family
>Mirad was living with
>but we found that
>he had disappeared
>the night before.
>He'd left his diary for us
>and on the last page was this letter:

FAZILA:
>Dear Uncle Djuka and Aunt Fazila.
>Today, 7th April 1993,
>exactly on my fourteenth birthday,
>I heard that Uncle Djuka is free
>and that you are coming to Holland too.
>I was more glad than I have been all my life.
>But afterwards I started thinking.
>Once you're here
>I could live with you
>and I could almost have a normal life
>because you are like a father and mother to me.
>But I don't want that.
>For maybe I still have a mother.
>That's why I decided to flee again.
>I'm going back to Foca to look for my mother,
>because if she is still alive
>she too has to start all over again some day.

And then she needs me.
I hope you understand
and you don't think I am ungrateful.
I didn't tell anybody because of my guardians.
I'm leaving tonight
without saying goodbye to anybody
like all refugees
everywhere in the world.
When I find my mother
or when I know what happened to her
I'll come back
or I'll phone
or I'll write.
Much love from your nephew Mirad Balic.

DJUKA:
Don't cry,
please don't cry.
He'll make it.
He is fourteen.
Anything can happen,
even a miracle.
Maybe he'll find his mother.
Could happen.
Come on.
Come on.
You must be strong.
Maybe everything will be all right.
Maybe we go back some day.
Start all over again.
Why not?
A lot of people do that.
Please,
don't cry

for then I'll start crying too
and then we'll never stop.
Come on
don't cry
please.

FAZILA:
We have to go.

DJUKA:
What?

FAZILA:
We have to go.

DJUKA:
Where to?

FAZILA:
Home.

DJUKA:
What home?

FAZILA:
Our home.

DJUKA:
Yes, of course.
We have to go home,
our own home.

FAZILA:
Sorry.
Sorry we have to go so soon.

DJUKA:
Yes sorry.

FAZILA:
Sorry we cannot stay any longer.

DJUKA:

That we weren't more pleasant.

FAZILA:

And that we carried on so much.

DJUKA:

Sorry.

FAZILA:

Yes sorry.

DJUKA:

But we have to go home.
To what's the name?

FAZILA:

To Heerhugowaard.

DJUKA:

Exactly.
Heerhugowaard.
We have to go home to Heerhugowaard.

FAZILA:

Come.
Come on.

DJUKA:

Yes, I am coming.

Part 2

Characters

MIRAD BALIC

VERICA BALIC-KOVAC, *Mirad's mother*

Prologue

VERICA:
> There are stories
> that nobody wants to tell
> and nobody wants to hear.

MIRAD:
> Stories that shouldn't be allowed to exist.

VERICA:
> But that will exist
> as long as there are people on earth.

MIRAD:
> In the old times
> when Yugoslavia was still a holiday land
> such stories used to start with:
> long ago
> in a far-away country.

VERICA:
> But now they start with:
> it happened in April 1992,
> on the market in Foca.

MIRAD:
> And they no longer tell about other people
> but about us.

VERICA:
> About a common mother,
> Verica.

MIRAD:
> And her son,
> Mirad.

VERICA:
> How that mother disappears
> on the first day of the war
> and only four months later returns,
> when Foca is in ruins
> and her husband and children
> are dead,
> according to her brother Milos.

MIRAD:
> The bastard.

VERICA:
> Ssst.

MIRAD:
> Isn't he?

VERICA:
> He is still your uncle.

MIRAD:
> If I see him
> I will kill him.

VERICA:
> You won't.

MIRAD:
> Filthy fascist.

VERICA:
> There has been enough murdering.
> The question is now how to go on,
> that's why we must break the silence.

MIRAD:
    The silence
    that surrounds us
    like a suffocating haze.

VERICA:
    Around us
    and our secrets,
    our terrible secrets.

MIRAD:
    Because this is also the story of a boy,
    a common boy
    who becomes a murderer.

VERICA:
    And yet he isn't.

MIRAD:
    Yes mother,
    just a murderer.

VERICA:
    Out of despair,
    like I wanted to kill my own child
    because I saw no way out.

MIRAD:
    But you didn't.

VERICA:
    No,
    I didn't,
    fortunately I didn't.

Scene 1

MIRAD:
  Hey
  you.
  Come here!

VERICA:
  When the Serbs drove into the market place,
  I'd run into a dead-end alley
  and I'd hidden myself behind a little building.

MIRAD:
  Yes, you!
  Who else?
  Come here, I say.

VERICA:
  But I was so afraid
  that I could only look.

MIRAD:
  Okay.
  I come to you.

VERICA:
  He couldn't be older than twenty
  and had a handsome face.

MIRAD:
  Don't look at me like that.
  I won't hurt you.
  Where is your headscarf?

VERICA:

I am not a Muslim.

MIRAD:

What are you then?

VERICA:

Serb.

MIRAD:

You don't say.
How old are you?

VERICA:

Thirty-four.

MIRAD:

Still good-looking.
Married?

VERICA:

Yes.

MIRAD:

To a Muslim?

VERICA:

No.
My husband is Serbian too.

MIRAD:

You're lying.
Children?

VERICA:

Two.
A boy and a girl.

MIRAD:

You're lying again.

VERICA:
  Mirad and Djelana.

MIRAD:
  Coat off!
  Watch out,
  as soon as you cry
  I'll shoot your head off.
  Coat off, I say!

VERICA:
  But I still couldn't move.

MIRAD:
  Think of your children.

VERICA:
  I took off my coat.

MIRAD:
  Turn,
  turn around.

VERICA:
  And suddenly that paralysing fear,
  that fear of years,
  it fell from my shoulders like a leaden coat.
  There it was,
  the war.
  I had always thought
  that it should have a monstrous,
  bloody face.
  But now it appeared to be
  an attractive young man
  with brown eyes and warm hands.
  I looked at the soldier
  and started to laugh softly:
  how old are you anyway?

MIRAD:

Shut up
or I'll shoot you.

VERICA:

Why?
What have I done?

MIRAD:

Shut up.
Turn around
if you want to see your children again.

VERICA:

I turned around slowly
and he started to pull at my skirt.
Opposite me a couple of pigeons sat on the edge of
a roof.
Far away there was shooting.
The wind brought a smell of fire
like sulphur.
Behind me I heard the soldier panting.
Fortunately Djelana and Mirad were at school,
the Serbs wouldn't attack any children.
Suddenly he stopped.
I looked back
and saw at a distance of three metres
a second soldier.
Help.
Help me.
But he didn't do anything.
He just stood there watching.
Then he came up to me
and hit me in the face
and dragged me

without a word
by my hair
out of the alley
into a truck.

Scene 2

MIRAD:
   I didn't know
   it would be so difficult
   to run away,
   to run away from home.
   Although it wasn't my real home
   but a foster family.
   It was still dark
   when I sneaked down the stairs,
   my heart beating in my mouth.
   I stayed awake almost the entire night
   but I'd waited until I heard the clock striking five.
   If my foster parents heard me,
   they would think I was going on my newspaper-
   round.
   When I passed the room of my foster brother,
   I wanted to go in
   to say goodbye.
   But I knew I shouldn't do that.
   The living room was still hung
   with the paper decorations for my birthday
   because yesterday I reached fourteen.
   They'd put them up in the middle of the night.
   It was meant to be a surprise
   but I had heard them pushing the ladder
   and quarrelling with each other
   over how to fix the strings.
   I got a big present:

a tennis racket.
They may as well return it now.
The table was ready for breakfast.
On my plate was my library card.
Hey, I lost it.
I sat down and started crying.
They wouldn't understand,
they'd think I wasn't happy with them.
Martijn would keep asking where I was
and when I would come back.
I felt lousy
but I had to do it,
now.
Before Uncle Djuka and Aunt Fazila would come,
for then I wouldn't be able to go any more.
I'd put my rucksack into the barn that night
with my clothes
and of course my walkman.
I'd earned that myself.
When I walked down the garden path
I started to cry again.
I thought I was a weakling
but I couldn't stop.
At the end of the street I halted
and looked back one more time.
I could go back.
If I went back now
and started delivering the newspapers,
nobody would ever know what I'd had in mind.
Then I'd wake up Martijn
and the four of us would have breakfast.
In the distance I saw a truck.
When it passed me, it went through a big puddle

and I got splashed with water.
And suddenly it was over.
It wasn't difficult any more.
Like a thread had been cut.
Suddenly I knew again
why I had to go back to Foca.
I wiped the mud from my clothes,
took my rucksack
and started walking.
It was Thursday, 8th April 1993,
half six in the morning.
Daylight was coming.

Scene 3

VERICA:
What do you want?

MIRAD:
Good morning, sir.
I am Mirad Kovac.
I am a refugee from Bosnia.

VERICA:
Congratulations.

MIRAD:
I am Serbian.
I want to go back.

VERICA:
Then I suggest you take a train.

MIRAD:
I thought that maybe you could help me.

VERICA:
How did you know my address?

MIRAD:
Someone from the refugee centre gave it to me, sir.
He had spoken to you
at the gate.
He said you were looking for people to do a job.

VERICA:
You're trying to fool me, boy.

MIRAD:
Not at all, sir.

But I thought that maybe I could do
something for you.

VERICA:

Get lost.

MIRAD:

He said it had to do with cars going to Serbia.

VERICA:

So what?

MIRAD:

I said he was wrong,
because of the boycott by the United Nations.
Nothing can enter Serbia,
not even cars.

VERICA:

And then, what did he say?

MIRAD:

That he was sure.
You said so.

VERICA:

Well,
did I say so?

MIRAD:

Yes, sir.
And I thought
maybe I could go in one of these cars.
I speak Serbo-croatian,
so I can interpret.

VERICA:

Why do you need to go back?

MIRAD:

I want to join the fighting, sir.

71

The Croats have murdered my whole family.

VERICA:

Wait here.
I'll talk to my boss.

MIRAD:

Thank you, sir.

Scene 4

VERICA:
> I couldn't see anything in the dark,
> but I felt
> that there was another person in the back
> of the truck.
> Maybe one of the soldiers,
> or even more than one.
> I held my breath
> and listened,
> but I didn't hear a thing.
> Not the slightest sound.
> The stories of my father
> drifted like poisonous vapours through my head.
> I had to try and stay calm,
> calm.

MIRAD:
> Two days passed before we left.
> They could use me
> but something had to be arranged,
> the man told me.
> And he locked me up in a small dark room
> with only a bed and a chair
> and a boarded up window.
> Twice a day the man brought me a tray with food.
> There were no books.
> After all
> I was not able to read
> because there was no light.

73

The batteries of my walkman were flat.
I didn't dare ask for new ones
and so I started to think again
of my mother
and of the stories of Grandpapa Kovac.

VERICA:
My father was born the eldest son
of a Serbian father and mother
in Croatia.
His family had lived there for ages.
When he was ten,
April 1941,
the Germans invaded Croatia.
Eleven days later the country had to surrender
and the Ustasji came to power,
a crowd of fascists
who wanted to exterminate or deport
all Serbs in Croatia.

MIRAD:
One day the Ustasji came to the village where grandfather lived.

VERICA:
It was a hot day in July.
Most men were working in the field
or in the factory,
while the women were at home
with the children.

MIRAD:
Nobody had seen them coming
but suddenly they were all around us.

VERICA:
My grandmother heard screaming and crying.

74

She looked out of the window
and saw an old man being dragged out of his house
by two soldiers.
They disappeared around the corner of the house.

MIRAD:

A moment later she heard a shot.

VERICA:

My grandmother ran to the door
and locked it.
After that she quickly closed the blinds.

MIRAD:

Then she took her three kids
down to the cellar.
And they sat as still as stones.

VERICA:

My father told me that he was so afraid,
his whole body was trembling.

MIRAD:

But his mother said:
'Stop it.
I say, stop it.
Are you a man?'
He was only ten.

VERICA:

Then the Ustasji started banging on the door.

MIRAD:

'Open up,'
they screamed.
'We know that Serbs live here.
Open up, immediately.'

VERICA:
>   For a moment there was silence.
>   Then a series of shots.
>   And with a thundering noise
>   the door was kicked in.

MIRAD:
>   'Come out,'
>   they shouted.
>   'We know you're at home.
>   Or shall we set the house on fire?'

VERICA:
>   'Watch the little ones,'
>   whispered my grandmother to my father.
>   'Take care that they don't make a sound.'

MIRAD:
>   Then she walked upstairs.

VERICA:
>   Six soldiers stood in the room.
>   She could hardly see their faces
>   because the only light came through
>   the battered door.

MIRAD:
>   She closed the cellar door
>   and said:
>   'What can I do for you?'

VERICA:
>   Stupid of course.
>   Who says such a thing?

MIRAD:
>   For a moment there was silence.
>   Then the men started laughing raucously,

'What can I do for you?
What can I do for you?'

VERICA:

When they stopped laughing
one of the soldiers said,
'Get her.'

MIRAD:

Four men seized her roughly.

VERICA:

She never was able to tell anybody
what happened next.

MIRAD:

They didn't even untie her
when they left.

VERICA:

'So your husband can see
what you're doing while he's gone,'
one of them said.
And then they started again
with their raucous laughter.

MIRAD:

In the meantime the shooting outside had stopped.

VERICA:

Down in the cellar
the youngest had fallen asleep on my father's lap.

MIRAD:

And after a while it was again as silent
as before the Ustasji had come.

VERICA:

When my father finally dared to go upstairs,
he saw his mother.

77

MIRAD:

He hardly dared to look.
He went to her.
Carefully he took the gag out of her mouth.

VERICA:

She didn't move,
only opened her eyes
and looked at her son.

MIRAD:

'Please let the little ones stay in the cellar,'
she whispered.

VERICA:

My father closed the cellar door quickly.

MIRAD:

'And tell nobody what you've seen,'
she said,
'not even your father.'

VERICA:

But he got to know of course.
How can you hide such a thing from your own
husband?

MIRAD:

The next day they decided to flee
to Serbia
before it was too late.

Scene 5

VERICA:
But it was already too late.
For my father it was already too late.
He was ten
and suddenly he was no longer a child.
Suddenly all children's dreams were over.
He'd looked into the mouth of the monster
and suddenly he had grown up.
He would never play with marbles any more.
And never be able to believe
in a future as a mountaineer or a football hero,
In future he would always have a knife under his pillow.
And behind well-meaning words
he would look for evil intentions.
His world had fallen apart
into good and evil.
The good people were us,
the evil people were them,
the Croatians,
the others.
And we could never mingle any more.
So when Milosevic started his campaign of hatred about ten years ago,
my father was ready to stoke the fire.
And when I married my husband,
a Muslim,
he didn't come to the wedding.

Scene 6

MIRAD:
Two days in a dark shed,
that's long
very long.
You have to watch out that you don't start
going crazy.
But it's also informative
because every minute of the day and the night
you're alone with yourself.
And so I discovered
that I didn't want to go to Foca
to look for my mother.
That's what I thought,
that's what I'd written to Uncle Djuka and Aunt
Fazila.
But it wasn't true.
I didn't believe any more
that my mother was still alive.
I just wanted to go back
to pay them off,
they'd have to pay for it,
the Serbs,
no matter how.
I didn't care
whether I lived or died
if I could do something.
When we were ready to leave
a big blue Mercedes drove up

with a sunroof and leather seats.
A real swanky car.
And suddenly I knew who it was for.
The evening before they had been talking together.
I had tried to listen
but I couldn't understand anything.
Only a name,
Arkan.
That's what they were talking about
all the time.
First I didn't know who he was
but then it came to my mind.
He was that war criminal
who had his own army in Bosnia.
I'd seen it on television.
That car was for him, of course,
they had stolen it.
And it had to be smuggled out to Serbia.
I suddenly lost my breath
and wanted to run away
but one of the men seized me by the arm
and said:
Hey,
where do you think you're going?
I have to go to the toilet, I said.
That's possible, he said,
but I'll go with you.
On the toilet I asked myself what I had to do.
If I drove with them
I would be helping the greatest murderer of Bosnia.
If I didn't
how did I get out of Holland?
Of course they'd sent out a trace order.

Are you coming? the man shouted.
I slowly got up,
flushed the toilet,
walked to the car
and sat down next to the driver.
Have a good journey,
said the man.
And call me
when you've thrown your first grenade.

Scene 7

VERICA:
    After all I shouldn't have been so afraid
    in the back of the truck.
    There were only some women like me.
    I think from Foca too,
    I didn't know them
    and we didn't speak with each other.
    Probably all four of us had the same horrible secret.
    Thank god we didn't stop on the way.
    We drove straight to a Serbian camp in the
    mountains
    and when we got out
    the first one I saw was my own brother Milos.

MIRAD:
    Jesus ...
    What are you doing here?

VERICA:
    I should ask you that.

MIRAD:
    Why didn't you say you're Serbian?

VERICA:
    I am not Serbian.

MIRAD:
    O no?
    What are you then?

VERICA:
    Yugoslavian.

MIRAD:
  Yugoslavia doesn't exist any more.

VERICA:
  That's what you say.

MIRAD:
  You're Serbian goddamn it.
  Who arrested you?

VERICA:
  Doesn't matter.

MIRAD:
  That's up to me.
  Who was it?
  What did he look like?
  What did he do?

VERICA:
  Do you really want to know?

MIRAD:
  If he's so much as put a finger on you,
  I'll kill him.

VERICA:
  That's very nice.
  You make me glad.

MIRAD:
  Well,
  who was it?

VERICA:
  Doesn't matter.
  You'd better help me get home.

MIRAD:
  Was it the tall one?
  or the fat one with that bald head?

VERICA:

Milos, please,
I only want to go back.

MIRAD:

You cannot go back.

VERICA:

What are you saying?

MIRAD:

You can't go back.

VERICA:

Why not?

MIRAD:

There's a war going on,
got it?

VERICA:

But you're my brother.

MIRAD:

What's that got to do with it?

VERICA:

You're the commander here,
or something like that.

MIRAD:

Exactly,
that's why.

VERICA:

You're not serious.

MIRAD:

I'm sorry but that's how it is.

VERICA:

You can't mean that, Milos.

MIRAD:

Did you think I'd let you go
because you're my sister?
A Serbian
married to a Muslim?
Did you think my men would accept that?

VERICA:

What a devil you are.

MIRAD:

I'll take care to get you to another camp.

VERICA:

You're evil.

MIRAD:

Keep calm.
You could have been in a women's hotel.

VERICA:

What kind of hotel?

MIRAD:

You know.

VERICA:

Milos Kovac,
that you're a son of a bitch
I've known for a long time.
But I didn't know you were that bad.

MIRAD:

A few weeks at the utmost
and Foca will be ours.
Then you can go back.

VERICA:

And I must believe that?

MIRAD:

In the meantime
I'll let your husband know where you are.

VERICA:

Did you ever keep a promise?

MIRAD:

Don't you believe it.

VERICA:

Milos, please,
take me back.
I beg you.
What would you think
if your children had to miss their mother?
Djelana and Mirad will not know where I am.
They are your family.

MIRAD:

My family only consists of Serbs,
one hundred per cent Serbs.

VERICA:

Fascist.
You have no mercy
for anyone.
I knew.
And if I try to escape?

MIRAD:

They'll shoot you.
Those are the instructions.

VERICA:

Your instructions.

MIRAD:
  Yes,
  my instructions.

VERICA:
  What camp is that?

MIRAD:
  For Serbs fleeing from Bosnia or Croatia.
  From there you can go to a foster family.

VERICA:
  When?

MIRAD:
  I'll see.

VERICA:
  Thank you, Milos.
  Thank you.
  If there is a God
  he'll reward you.

Scene 8

MIRAD:
   Call me Patrick,
   said the man who drove the Mercedes.
   And if they ask anything at the border
   your name is Ratko Lipovic
   and you speak only Serbo-croatian.
   I am a friend of your father
   and I am taking you home.
   In the dashboard is your passport.
   I looked at my watch
   and saw it was almost eleven.
   Saturday, 10th April 1993.
   The hour 22.58.
   Within half an hour we would be out of Holland.
   Maybe I would never come back.
   I thought of Martijn,
   of Abdul and Rostam
   and of my foster parents.
   When I heard the Dutch language for the first time,
   it sounded like a secret language.
   But I'd learned it rather good in those seven months.
   Maybe I could become an interpreter in the future –
   if there was to be a future.
   Somewhere in Germany Patrick started to boast
   that he knew Arkan, the tiger,
   from the time they were together in jail,
   in 1981.
   Both for a couple of armed robberies.

Arkan got seven years,
he four.
Then they'd come up with a plan to escape,
together.
I looked out of the window,
we drove through a mountainous landscape.
I thought of all the times
I drove with our neighbour from Foca.
He was a truck-driver.
So, when I was seven
I wanted to become a truck-driver too.
If I didn't have to go to school
he took me with him.
I sat the whole day next to him in the cabin
on an upside down beer crate.
The whole world passed like a movie,
our whole Yugoslavia
with all the mountains and woods,
rivers and fields,
villages and valleys.
Don't you want to know how we tried to escape?
asked Patrick.
Of course, I said.
And then he started a whole story about accomplices
and a gun that was thrown over the wall of the jail.
Finally Arkan had escaped.
Not he.
But that was sheer bad luck.
Would he still be alive,
our neighbour?
He had fought till the last moment to defend Foca.
He must have been sent also to such a camp,
just like Uncle Djuka and me.

Later.
I felt my ribs.
I looked at Patrick
and thought,
Shall I stab him
with my penknife
while he is asleep?
But then I realised he was just a follower.
It wasn't about him
but about those who started this war.
At the border with Hungary
Patrick went on with his crazy talking:
Do you know he is now in Bosnia,
the tiger?
There he has an army of three thousand Serbian
volunteers.
Arkan's tigers,
that's what they call themselves.
They were about the first ones
that started cleaning the Muslims.
You call that ethnic cleansing.
Didn't you see that picture in *Time Magazine*
how they killed Muslims
with those black caps over their heads?
Like pigs.
No boy,
that Arkan is hard.
You can learn a lot from him.
So do I.
When I've delivered this car
I'll join those tigers for a while.
Could be fun.

Scene 9

VERICA:

    How often my father told it to us
    I don't know any more,
    innumerable times
    over and over again he had to tell it,
    we couldn't stand it any more.
    How he had fled as a boy from Croatia
    and he wasn't allowed to say goodbye to
    anyone.
    Not even Josip,
    his best friend.

MIRAD:

    When Grandfather Kovac told a story
    I was always jealous.
    When he was ten he'd experienced a lot,
    his life seemed an exciting book
    with all kinds of dangerous adventures.
    While my life was just boring
    for Foca was really a hole of a place,
    nothing ever happened there.

VERICA:

    Josip and his parents are Croatians,
    we can't be careful enough, boy,
    his mother told him.
    Our life depends on it.

MIRAD:

    When it was dark

and everybody in the village was asleep,
they had sneaked out of the door.

VERICA:

It was a clear night.

MIRAD:

Without a word
they walked through the village.

VERICA:

My father knew that he'd never come back here.

MIRAD:

When they passed the house of Josip
he could hardly keep back his tears.

VERICA:

But then he thought again
of his mother's words in the cellar.

MIRAD:

Stop,
stop I say!
Are you a man?

VERICA:

A little outside the village the woods began
and after a while
they reached an open space.

MIRAD:

There some hundred people were waiting.
Twenty families,
they all had the same little luggage with them.
Only a few blankets,
some furniture
and some food.

VERICA:

My father knew them all
he had only never known
that they were Serbs.

MIRAD:

One man he didn't know,
that man went to all the groups
to receive a little packet.

VERICA:

A packet of banknotes,
for that man is our guide,
said my grandmother later to my father.
We have to be grateful to him.

MIRAD:

The journey would last for about a week,
walking.
And they would have to walk mainly through
the woods and along mountain paths
to make sure they were not seen by the Ustasji.

VERICA:

The first days all went well
but on the fourth day the guide said
that now the most dangerous part of the
journey began.

MIRAD:

They had to go through a narrow strip of woods
about ten kilometres in length
and not even three hundred metres wide.

VERICA:

At one side of the wood there was a river.
At the other side there was a big army camp of
the Ustasji.

MIRAD:

They had to walk as fast as possible
and not to make the slightest noise,
otherwise they would be caught for sure.

VERICA:

And what would happen then,
nobody dared think of it.

MIRAD:

There were rumours that a previous group of
refugees
was caught because a child had been crying.

VERICA:

All of them were said to have been murdered,
their bodies thrown in the river.

MIRAD:

Whether that was true
the guide didn't want to tell,
but neither did he want to go with the refugees
through the woods.
he would meet them at the other side,
he said.

VERICA:

Fifty years later
my father knew exactly how it happened.

MIRAD:

When they were halfway through the wood
there was a sudden shot.

VERICA:

Everybody started to run in panic,
but my father's youngest brother,

who had fallen asleep in the arms of my
grandmother,
woke up suddenly and started to cry loudly.

MIRAD:

Everybody ran on
because the guide had said
they should never stop.

VERICA:

My grandmother tried to keep with them
as best she could while trying feverishly
to think what she had to do.

MIRAD:

Maybe the Ustasji were very close.
If the child kept crying
everybody would be betrayed.

VERICA:

My grandfather walked the whole journey
at the front with the other men,
so he couldn't help her.

MIRAD:

Suddenly she took a blanket
and pressed it to the face of her son.

VERICA:

The crying stopped.
My grandmother ran and stumbled on
but when she tried to loosen the blanket
carefully,
the crying started again.
So she pushed the blanket back again.

MIRAD:

Nobody knew how long she'd run like that,

but finally the file slowed down a bit.

VERICA:

Then my father saw
that his mother cried terribly though she made no
sound.
Tears were coursing down her face.

MIRAD:

He walked up to her
but didn't dare to say anything.

VERICA:

After a while she opened the blanket
and walking on she showed my father
the face of his little brother.

MIRAD:

It was blue
and very silent.

VERICA:

Then my grandmother gave her dead child
a kiss on the forehead,
closed the blanket again
and placed it on the roadside.

MIRAD:

Far away they could see the end of the woods.

VERICA:

She gave my father her hand.

MIRAD:

And so they walked on.

Scene 10

VERICA:
> To lose a child,
> I've always thought,
> is the worst thing that could happen to a woman.
> But to get a child
> can be as horrible.
> For six weeks I didn't notice anything.
> Milos had let me be brought to a poor refugee camp
> in Serbia.
> There I heard that Foca was under permanent siege
> and that nobody could get in or out of the city.
> During the shooting there were many dead
> and wounded people.
> I was desperate.
> Whole days I walked like a mad woman through the
> camp.
> I asked everybody
> whether they knew anything about my
> husband and my children.
> But nobody knew anything.
> Or they didn't want to tell.
> Of the Serbian soldier I didn't think for one
> moment.
> And then came that horrible May the 20th.
> The whole day I had been terribly nervous,
> I was terrified of every noise
> and I trembled constantly.
> I didn't know what had come over me,

until I realised that I should have had my
period long ago.
It was like somebody hit my head with a brick.
If I was pregnant
it was him,
the soldier.
I felt my whole body stiffen.
I sat on the edge of my bed
and waited,
waited,
waited.
But nothing happened.
And slowly
but irrevocably
the knowledge came to me
that my belly gave room to a tumour,
a tumour
that would grow into a child of the war.
That the enemy
finally penetrated my body.
Fifty years ago my father
had looked into the mouth of the monster,
now it was my turn.

Scene 11

VERICA:
    So you are that boy
    that came from Holland.

MIRAD:
    Yes sir.

VERICA:
    Sir?
    I am no sir.
    Here on the battlefield my name is Arkan.
    For everybody,
    also for you.
    Do you know what that means?

MIRAD:
    Yes.
    Tiger.

VERICA:
    Exactly.
    You've got that from the papers?

MIRAD:
    No.
    Patrick told me.

VERICA:
    Patrick, who?

MIRAD:
    The driver.

VERICA:
    O, that pig.
    Nice car, isn't it?
    What's your name anyway?

MIRAD:
    Ratko Lipovic.

VERICA:
    I saw that in your passport,
    a professional job.
    But now your real name.

MIRAD:
    Mirad.

VERICA:
    Mirad?
    Is that Serbian?

MIRAD:
    Yes.

VERICA:
    Never heard of it.
    And your second name?

MIRAD:
    Kovac.

VERICA:
    That's better.
    Mirad Kovac.
    Strange anyway.
    Related to commander Milos Kovac?

MIRAD:
    That's my uncle.

VERICA:
    Ahhh.

There we are.
And when do you become a volunteer?

MIRAD:

I am only fourteen.

VERICA:

I don't mind.
One afternoon's training
and you can throw a grenade.
Or do you already know how such a thing works?

MIRAD:

No.

VERICA:

Then stay here for a couple of days
and the boys will explain everything to you.

MIRAD:

But I have to go to Foca.

VERICA:

What for?

MIRAD:

To my mother.

VERICA:

Does she live there?

MIRAD:

Yes.

VERICA:

And your father?

MIRAD:

Also.
But he is dead.
Shot by the Muslims.

VERICA:

Again a reason to get them by the ears.
How would you get there?

MIRAD:

Don't know yet.

VERICA:

Within a week a patrol goes in that direction.
You can go with them.
Until then you stay here
to join the training of the recruits.
A Serbian boy of fourteen
who can't handle weapons,
impossible.

MIRAD:

Yes sir.
All right sir.

Scene 12

VERICA:
From that day on time was a trap.
Every hour I planned
to drown myself in the river.
Me and that terrible child.
But when I stood on the bank
I remembered all the times
I'd sat with Mirad and Djelana
on the banks of the Drina,
and my feet refused to go further.
Time was a trap
and my belly a time bomb.
One night I tried to get rid of the little monster
with a hot knitting needle
but I fainted.
And afterwards
the other women guarded me,
like I was an insane person.
In the meantime the war grew
together with my fear:
would my children still be alive?
What would my husband say
when he heard what happened to me?
Would our house still exist?
Our camp grew more and more crowded.
Every day I heard about acts of horror
done by Croatians and Muslims,
worse than in the stories my father told.

There was an enormous shortage of everything:
food, clothes, baby-food, toys, medicines,
and nobody helped us.
Later I heard
that the Western countries helped all refugees,
except those in Serbia.
And then,
on 30th July 1992,
Milos came to the camp.
I saw him coming from far away
and my world fell apart.

MIRAD:

I am sorry,
I am sorry Verica.

VERICA:

Now he,
that terrible brother,
was the only thing I still had.

MIRAD:

They're dead,
all three.

VERICA:

And that terrible baby of course.
I still had that.

MIRAD:

Do you hear me?

VERICA:

That would pay for all that,
be sure.

MIRAD:

They're dead all three.

VERICA:

Within five months it would crawl out of my belly,
that child of the devil.

MIRAD:

Don't you want to know how it happened?

VERICA:

If it came out,
I would strangle it with its own umbilical cord.

MIRAD:

Verica.

VERICA:

After that I could finally walk into the water.

MIRAD:

Your husband and your children are dead.
But you can go back to Foca.

VERICA:

Because what mother can
at the same time
get a child
and lose two others?

MIRAD:

Your house is still there.

VERICA:

Yes, yes.
My house is still there.
Then I didn't say anything any more
for five months.
Not a word passed my lips.
My brother took me to Foca.
There I lived in my own house

like the ruins
of somebody that had existed.
And out of the window
I saw the remains
of a city
that had existed.
And all the time I carried
together with an inhuman embryo
an inhuman silence within me.
A silence that consisted of hatred and despair
which only cracked
when the pain became unbearable,
the night of his birth.

Scene 13

MIRAD:
Two days before the patrol was due to leave
I knew it.
It was a terrible plan,
but it didn't leave me.
Finally I would pay them off.
The training of the tigers was disgusting.
They showed you
how you could cut someone's throat
with only one strike of a hunting knife.
Or how you could burn with only one flamethrower
a whole row of people at the same time.
But I kept alert.
Between Sokolac and Rogatica,
about eighty kilometres from Foca,
it finally happened.
It was Tuesday, 20th April 1993,
12.30 in the afternoon.
We drove in an open jeep of the former
Yugoslavian army.
The patrol consisted of three young soldiers
of about twenty
and one elderly man
who went on all the time
about the Muslims wanting to create
an Islamic state in Bosnia.
The others didn't even listen,
they spoke only about football.

Before they became tigers
they were just like Arkan,
fanatical supporters of Red Star Belgrado.
One of them had just got a daughter.
He hadn't even seen her
but he had pictures.
All of us had to look.
He had a very young wife.
When they got hungry
the driver went up a track through the woods
and stopped at a beautiful spot.
They took their provisions
and started eating.
I'd said I was sleepy
and I wanted to lie down a while in the jeep.
Through my whimpers I looked at the soldiers.
They sat close together
at a distance of about fifteen metres from the jeep.
I only had one grenade.
I had to throw it right the first time.
I drew the pin
and stood straight up in the jeep.
A fraction of a second I doubted.
If I didn't throw
I wouldn't be alive any more within the count of
four.
Get rid of everything.
But my arm didn't hesitate.
I threw the grenade and dived down.
For a moment there was a silence,
then an enormous bang.
After that nothing.
Carefully I left the jeep.

It was a horrifying sight,
the spot where the soldiers had been.
I turned around and started to walk to Foca.
I tried to feel proud and satisfied.
I'd taken revenge for my father and sister
but I felt nothing but sick and tired.
I realised that nothing had changed.
I killed four men
and everything had stayed the same.

Scene 14

VERICA:
When labour started,
on the evening of 31st December 1992,
I didn't call for anybody,
but closed the doors
and the blinds.
My teeth clamped tight,
I prepared everything,
decided to bring this tumour
into the world in silence,
in order to let it disappear
after that in another
still deeper silence.
For hours the pain beat against my body
like the hatred and the sadness did
against my soul for months.
When the pain seemed to win through the silence,
I put a gag in my mouth
and bound a shawl over it.
And so I waited for the most terrifying moment.
For years I'd been frightened of the war,
now I was the war myself.
Then the evil took its last run,
and in a hurricane of sweat and blood
I felt my belly emptying itself.
And I sank away
in a sadness so big
that it became a mercy.

At last I heard somewhere far away a soft crying.
I came to
and saw something lying between my legs.
It wasn't a monster,
no devil,
no tumour,
but a human being.
A child,
a little boy.
I took it
and laid it against my breast.
And I knew
I would live on.

Scene 15

MIRAD:
   It took me two days to come from Rogatica to Foca.
   They were the most horrible days of my life.
   I could only think of the soldiers
   I'd killed.
   That the little daughter of that one soldier
   would never know her father.
   And his wife was a widow now,
   although she was only seventeen.
   When I arrived in Foca
   I immediately saw
   that the mosque had disappeared,
   raised to the ground.
   I walked into our street
   and was stupefied by what I saw:
   that our house was still there.
   I walked around
   and saw nappies and baby-clothes
   hanging on the clothes line
   of Serbians who took our house of course.
   And then the door opened.

VERICA:
   I was just busy with the laundry.
   I walked outside to hang something on the line.
   Then I saw a boy standing
   at the other side of the street.
   He reminded me of Mirad.

He looked pale and filthy and kept staring at the
house.

MIRAD:

A woman came outside
with a baby on her arm
and a bucket of laundry.
She looked the same height as my mother
but more skinny.
Much more skinny.

VERICA:

For a moment I thought
maybe it's Mirad.
But people always think that
if somebody they loved is dead.

MIRAD:

The woman started to hang the laundry
with one hand,
very clumsy.
Just as clumsy as my mother.
And she kept looking back
like she saw a ghost.

VERICA:

I couldn't help it
but through my tears
I had to look at him,
again and again.

MIRAD:

I got a very strange feeling,
like that woman
was really my mother.
But that was impossible

because my mother was much fatter.
And she didn't have a baby.

VERICA:

Suppose Milos told me a lie.

MIRAD:

Suddenly I started walking to her
slowly
just like that.
I didn't know why.

VERICA:

That could be possible,
he used to tell lies.

MIRAD:

And with every step
that feeling got stronger.

VERICA:

When I turned around
the boy was very close.
He stood at a distance of only three metres
and he said only one word –

MIRAD:

Mama.

Epilogue

MIRAD:
    Mama,
    do you think the war will soon be over?

VERICA:
    I don't know.
    When is a war over?
    If there is no shooting any more
    or there is no more hatred?

MIRAD:
    Do you still think often of Papa?

VERICA:
    Every day.

MIRAD:
    And of Djelana?

VERICA:
    The same.

MIRAD:
    How can we live normal lives?

VERICA:
    We live on,
    but not normally.

MIRAD:
    I went fishing today in the Drina
    and I didn't think of them for a moment.

VERICA:
    That's how it goes,

that's how it should go.

MIRAD:

And you?
Do you ever forget?

VERICA:

Not yet,
but I will.

MIRAD:

Will you come with me to the spot
where I buried Papa's hand?

VERICA:

Yes, yes I promise.
Come and sit next to me.
Did you write already to Uncle Djuka and Aunt
Fazila?

MIRAD:

Of course,
and also Martijn.

VERICA:

Good.
Tell me,
when the war is over,
what are you going to do?

MIRAD:

I am going to work, I think.
Earn money
for the three of us.

VERICA:

I would like you to go to school again.
You wanted to become a journalist,
just like Uncle Djuka.

117

MIRAD:

Who is there to take care of you?

VERICA:

I can do that myself.
I am only thirty-five.
I am not an old woman.
Or isn't that your dream any more,
to be a journalist.

MIRAD:

Yes.

VERICA:

Well,
and when you have finished your studies,
you know what you have to do?

MIRAD:

No.

VERICA:

Write the story of this war.
So that nobody will forget
how terrible
and how senseless it was.
You agree?

MIRAD:

I agree.

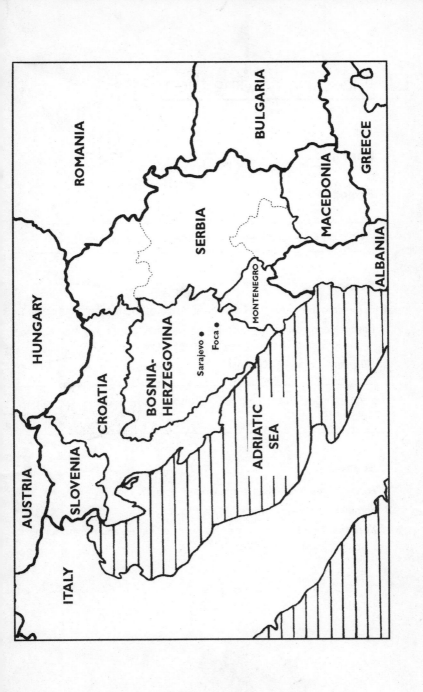

Glossary: reading the text

Part 1

Prologue

Why do Fazila and Djuka repeat several times the word 'sorry'?

Scene 1

4 *Serbo-croatian*   the chief official language of the former Yugoslavia.

5 *Bosnia-Herzegovina*   one of the republics in former Yugoslavia, now an independent state (see map page 119).

Flüchtling   refugee (German).

What does this scene tell us about how refugees are often treated?

Scene 2

7 *Foca*   a town in Bosnia, pronounced 'Focha'.

8 *Somalia*   a country in north-east Africa.

Kurdish   largely nomadic people living in Turkey and neighbouring middle-eastern countries.

> 1 What does Mirad mean when he writes, 'The people here are nice but they seem to be behind a thick glass wall'?
> 2 Why might a Somalian and a Kurdish boy be in the same house as Mirad?

Scene 3

9 *Sarajevo* capital city of Bosnia-Herzegovina.

Serbia and Montenegro former Yugoslavian republics, now independent states (see map, page 119).

1 *Communism* the form of government in Yugoslavia before the break-up of the USSR and the coming of independence.

5 *liberators* those who free others from something or someone.

> 1 What does Djuka tell us about the effects of Communism on the people?
> 2 What do we learn about the attitudes of ordinary people as civil war approaches?

Scene 4

6 *orthodox* Christian Orthodox New Year: 1 January.

Nenad Pejic a community spokesman for the people of Bosnia.

> Why is Mirad particularly moved by the occasion when everybody in Sarajevo switched off their lights?

Scene 5

9 *freelance journalist* working for different newspapers.

21 *violation*   breaking, disregarding.

22 *Holy Peter*   the Holy Catholic Church.

Do you admire Djuka's silence in the face of terrible threats?

Scene 6

23 *Cambodia*   country in south-east Asia, with a history of being invaded and therefore having many war refugees.

24 *asylum*   under international law someone who thinks they are in danger in their own country can request political asylum – and safety – in another country.

What kind of mood is Mirad in as he writes in this scene?

Scene 7

25 *Allah*   the main Muslim name for God, the Supreme Being.

  Tito   President of Yugoslavia (1953–80).

26 *impenetrable*   cannot be understood.

What view of religions comes across from Djuka in this scene?

Scene 8

30 *shrapnel*   fragments exploding from the mortar bombs.

How does the writer create a sense of both horror and sadness in describing Djelana's death?

Scene 9

> 1   What does the playwright say here about hate and revenge?

Scene 10

6 *curfew*   a time when movement is restricted, especially at night during wartime.

10 *Keraterm*   one of the internment camps.

> 1   What do we learn about the impact of the civil war on Mirad's family?
> 2   Why do you think Mirad was released to go to Holland?

Scene 11

2 *'technical expedition'*   a term used to hide the truth of what is about to happen.

> What are your feelings at the end of reading this scene?

Scene 12

5 *International Red Cross*   a long-established organisation that offers medical support around the world, particularly in times of war and natural disasters.

> Why does the writer conclude this scene with the words, 'There I saw Fazila for the first time in nine months'?

Scene 13

48 *carbolic soap*   disinfectant soap.
50 *hospitable*   welcoming.

> How do Fazila and Djuka react to one another?

Scene 14

55 *Heerhugowaard*   a town about fifty kilometres north of
Amsterdam.

> 1   What is your reaction to Mirad's leaving for Foca?
> 2   Why does the writer end the play with Djuka and Fazila saying
> 'sorry' to the audience?

Part 2

Prologue

> What does Verica mean when she says, 'The question is now how
> to go on'?

Scene 1

> What does Verica mean when she says, 'that fear of years, it fell
> from my shoulders like a leaden coat'?

Scene 2

8 *Martijn*   Mirad's foster brother.

> How do Mirad's emotions change in this scene?

Scene 3

I *boycott*   refusal to deal with someone or something.

> How does Mirad hope to escape from Holland?

Scene 4

3 *vapours*   mist or smoke.
4 *Ustasji*   extreme Croatian nationalists.
  exterminate   to destroy completely.
6 *raucously*   harshly.

> How is history shown to repeat itself horribly in this scene?

Scene 5

9 *Milosevic*   leader of the Serbian Communists.

> What, according to this scene, is the effect of war on childhood dreams?

Scene 6

81 *swanky*   posh.

Arkan   leader of the Serbian Volunteer Guard, popularly known as the 'Tigers'.

a trace order   a search warrant for Mirad.

> Why does the writer end this scene with the words, 'And call me when you've thrown your first grenade'?

Scene 7

> What aspect of civil war does the meeting in this scene reinforce? Compare scene 10 in Part 1.

Scene 8

90 *accomplices*   people who help others to commit a crime.

91 *ethnic cleansing*   murdering people because of their ethnic background.

> What are the two stories that are running parallel in this scene?

Scene 9

92 *innumerable*   countless.

97 *coursing*   running.

> How does the writer convey the plight of the refugee in this scene? What echoes from Part 1 do you hear?

Scene 10

9 *irrevocably*   cannot be changed.

> How does this scene link with others earlier in the play?

Scene 11

> What kind of thumb-nail sketch of Arkan is given here?

Scene 12

7 *inhuman*   cruel.

> What is meant by Verica in saying, 'From that day on time was a trap'?

Scene 13

8 *Sokolac and Rogatica*   towns near Foca.
Islamic state   a country governed by the religion of Islam.
9 *Red Star Belgrado*   famous football team.
provisions   food.

> How does Mirad react to his killing of the soldiers?

Scene 14

What emotions are experienced by Verica in the last stages of her pregnancy?

Scene 15

113 *stupefied* amazed.

What echoes are there in this scene of the meeting between Djuka and Fazila in Part 1, scene 13?

Epilogue

116 *Drina* main river that flows through Foca.

Do you feel that the play ends on an optimistic note?

Study programme

Characters

In drama and fiction it is important to remember that a writer may well 'load the dice' about a character's personality and attitudes. In shaping your own views about a stage character, think about:

- what the character does, and how s/he behaves towards others and in different situations;
- what the character says, when and to whom;
- what others say about the character.

Fazila and Djuka

1 Look back carefully through the play. Make a list of quotations that help you form a clear picture of both Fazila and Djuka. Organise them in two columns on a sheet of paper:

Fazila	Djuka

Use the above notes to write a short character description of each of them.

2 Make notes on Fazila's and Djuka's life in Holland. Look carefully at what they each say in the play. Imagine you are a journalist writing a feature article on the couple for an international magazine. Draft out your piece and then rewrite a final copy – complete with eye-catching title – using a word-processor if possible.

3 How do their attitudes and emotions change in the course of the play? Look back over the text and make notes with accompanying quotations. Look in particular for moments when either of them is feeling particularly pessimistic or optimistic about the future.

4 Working in pairs, take it in turns to interview Fazila and Djuka about their experiences and feelings. In particular, how does their separation affect them? Tape your conversations and then write up the transcripts.

5 Put yourself in the place of either Fazila or Djuka ten years after the events described in the play. Write your thoughts and memories of what happened to you and your family. What are your feelings now? Where are you now living? Present your thoughts in the form of a monologue to others in your group.

6 Imagine you are Mirad on the eve of going back to Foca, April 1993. What are your thoughts about Uncle Djuka and Aunt Fazila? Write a few entries in your diary about your time with them in Sarajevo. What will you most remember about them as people?

Verica

7 Make a list of quotations that help establish a full picture of Verica. Use these to write a short character description.

8 Look back through the play. Note down what seem to you to have been the key 'turning points' in Verica's life. Think about how her emotions change in the course of her terrible personal experiences. At which particular moments is she hopeful or full of despair?

Now write some extracts from Verica's autobiography, using the 'I' narrator.

9 Imagine you are interviewing Verica some years after the end of the play for an article about the impact of war on family life. Working in pairs, draft out the interview; then perform it to others in your group.

Mirad

10 The following information is a chronological account of Mirad's
14th year. Look back through Part 1 of the play and complete the
date chart.

Event in play	Date
• Mirad's 13th birthday.	7 April 1992
• Independence of Bosnia declared. The Serbs invade his home town of Foca. His mother disappears.	
• His sister Djelana is killed by mortar shrapnel.	
• Imprisoned in Foca with his father.	
• He sees his father blown up by a mine. He, alone, escapes the massacre.	
• He reaches Sarajevo, 90 km. away, after walking for four nights.	
• Imprisoned with Uncle Djuka in camp Keraterm outside Sarajevo.	
• Released from the camp and sent to Holland as an International Red Cross refugee.	
• Arrives in Nunspeet, Holland, and placed in the Valentijn home for refugee children from war zones who have neither relatives nor friends.	
• Asks for political asylum, which, being over 12, he is permitted to do.	
• His application is successful on his giving a full description of the fate of his mother and father.	
• Moves out of Valentijn to live with a Dutch family.	
• Mirad's 14th birthday. He runs away from his guardians by night 'to look for my mother, because if she is still alive she too has to start all over again some day. And then she needs me'.	7 April 1993

11 Are there any dates and events mentioned in Part 1 which do not fit within the above time framework? Scan back through the text to see if you can add any details to the above.

12 Now draw up a time chart with the key events of Part 2 listed. Remember that the second part of the play covers a much longer period of time in Mirad's family history. The family tree on page 133 will help you.

13 As Mirad does not appear in person in Part 1 of the play, our picture of him must come from his letters and what his aunt and uncle say about him. Make a list of what you think are key quotations which describe his personality.

14 Now carry out a similar task, this time concentrating on Mirad's *emotions* at different points in his story. Make a note of where you think he must have been at his most depressed, angry, or hopeful. This could be drawn out on a large sheet of paper for classroom display. Make sure you use quotations from the text to support your opinions.

15 From your reading of Part 2, is the picture you have formed of Mirad in Part 1 in any way changed or added to? What do you think are the key moments in Mirad's journey in search of his mother?

16 'I realised that nothing had changed. I killed four men and everything had stayed the same' (page 110). Use these words as a starting point for a series of entries in Mirad's diary over the days which follow scene 13.

17 It is ten years later and Mirad is being interviewed as part of a television documentary on the war in Bosnia. Working in pairs, draft out a script of questions and answers that help to bring out Mirad's memories and reflections on civil war. Use a cassette or video recorder, if available.

Mirad's family

18 Study the following family tree. Look back through the play and note down quotations which refer to any of the family members. Then select one or two of the family who do not appear on stage in the play and tell *their* story of the civil war. Draft out some ideas. You will obviously need to use your imagination and research skills.

Now write up your notes as either a piece of biography or autobiography.

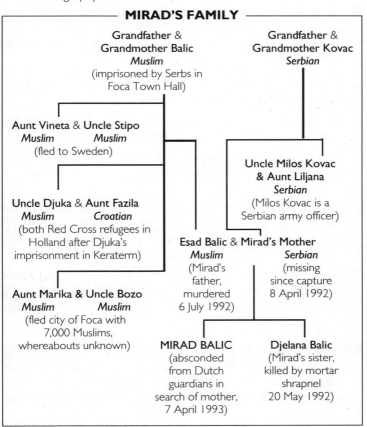

MIRAD'S FAMILY

Grandfather & Grandmother Balic
Muslim
(imprisoned by Serbs in Foca Town Hall)

Grandfather & Grandmother Kovac
Serbian

Aunt Vineta & Uncle Stipo
Muslim   Muslim
(fled to Sweden)

Uncle Milos Kovac & Aunt Liljana
Serbian
(Milos Kovac is a Serbian army officer)

Uncle Djuka & Aunt Fazila
Muslim   Croatian
(both Red Cross refugees in Holland after Djuka's imprisonment in Keraterm)

Esad Balic & Mirad's Mother
Muslim   Serbian
(Mirad's father, murdered 6 July 1992)   (missing since capture 8 April 1992)

Aunt Marika & Uncle Bozo
Muslim   Muslim
(fled city of Foca with 7,000 Muslims, whereabouts unknown)

MIRAD BALIC
(absconded from Dutch guardians in search of mother, 7 April 1993)

Djelana Balic
(Mirad's sister, killed by mortar shrapnel 20 May 1992)

In performance

[1] Write a set of notes for the actors playing Aunt Fazila, Uncle Djuka, Verica and Mirad. What kind of people are they playing? How should they present themselves to an audience? What should they be wearing? What problems might they encounter in their parts? Your detailed guide should attempt to capture the essence of each character.

[2] Director John Retallack writes (page 136): 'Though it is clearly a play that is of the utmost value to young audiences, I was shaken to read a good play on a subject that threatens to overpower the writer'.

What emotions did you experience as you were reading the play? Were there moments when you felt:

anger   hate   happy   sympathy   pity   helpless
tearful   overpowered   shame?

Look again carefully at the text to remind yourself how the telling of events affects our emotional reactions.

[3] One of the great strengths of the play is the simplicity of the language used and the rhythm of the writing. Read Ad de Bont's comments on the play's language (page x). In pairs, practise reading certain extracts to try and capture the appropriate tone and mood. Think carefully about the emotions and experiences that lie behind the words. When you are well rehearsed, present your performance to others in the group.

[4] Parts 1 and 2 of **Mirad** were written to be staged either on their own or together. Study the structure of each part and how subjects and phrases in Part 1 are skilfully echoed in Part 2. Make a list of these 'echoes'. Discuss how you would highlight them in a production.

5 Imagine you are directing the play. There are no printed stage directions and there are only four characters. How will you keep the audience's attention and ensure an engaging and entertaining production?

In pairs or small groups, working closely with the text, plan out the following with detailed notes and drawings.

- Do you want to stage the play 'in the round' or on a more formal raised stage?
- Where should each character be positioned on stage in each scene?
- How will you begin and end each scene to ensure the right rhythm to the play?
- What props do you need and how will they be used and moved around the stage?
- What sound effects will you employ?
- What devices will you use to help the audience follow the events of the war and Mirad's journey?
- Will you stage Parts 1 and 2 in different ways.

Now try staging two or three scenes, using the notes you have made to guide your stage direction.

6 Using the material in this book and any additional library research, produce a theatre programme which includes the following:

- a cast-list and one-paragraph description of each character;
- an introduction from the director;
- a brief summary of the play;
- a page of background notes on the war in Bosnia;
- a couple of short extracts from the diaries of Bosnian villagers;
- illustrations and/or photographs;
- newspaper accounts of the civil war.

By way of comparison, the programme for the first UK production of *Mirad, A Boy from Bosnia* contained the following information.

Introduction

Ad de Bont is well-known in Europe, particularly in Holland and
Germany, as one of the leading writers of plays for young people.
Theatre for young people is advanced – and funded – to a degree that
we cannot really imagine in Britain. Ad de Bont's company Wederzijds is
in the vanguard of this theatre movement. I first saw *MIRAD* – on its
second reading – in a classroom of ten and eleven year olds in an
outlying suburb of Amsterdam, in October '93. I expressed my enthu-
siasm to Ad de Bont. Three weeks later an English translation came
through my door.

Though it is clearly a play that is of the utmost value to young audiences,
I was shaken to read a good play on a subject that threatens to
overpower the writer. His focus on the child caught up in this indescrib-
ably savage war has cleared his imagination where others have remained
blocked, or simply frightened of the subject. Since October 1993, the
play has been picked up by over twenty German theatre companies, six
in Holland, and others all over Europe. All of these companies perform
exclusively for young people. This is the first performance in English.

John Retallack
Artistic Director
Oxford Stage Company
January 1994

BRITISH RED CROSS:
AID TO FORMER YUGOSLAVIA

Since the beginning of the conflict the International Red Cross, together with the National Societies of countries such as the UK, has worked with the local Red Cross in Former Yugoslavia to identify the most urgent needs of the people and respond promptly to them. The network of this worldwide movement enables the Red Cross to ensure that any aid sent into the country reaches its destination using local Red Cross members to distribute the goods on the ground. The British Red Cross itself has 35 delegates working in Former Yugoslavia.

During 1993, the Red Cross provided the following aid:

- Renovation of part of the water system to Sarajevo from Pale in Serb held territory
- Dialysis programme in Banja Luka in Bosnia to assist over 100 patients needing dialysis
- Food aid to 600,000 people each month in Bosnia
- 260 medical facilities across Bosnia-Herzegovina
- One hot meal a day to 15,000 of Sarajevo's most vulnerable residents
- Refurbishment of Kosevo hospital in Sarajevo
- Assistance to refugees throughout the country
- Processing of some 2 million messages and tracings for family members
- Rebuilding a school in Croatia in August with BBC's 'Challenge Anneka'
- Hygiene parcels, and infant care parcels – in Serbia and Croatia

---

Themes and issues

1 The play addresses – more or less directly – the following issues. Which are most powerfully conveyed to you?

- the effects of civil war on friends and neighbours
- one family's story of war

- the power of love between mother and son
- the Bosnian conflicts of the 1990s
- the plight of refugees
- the brutality and pity of war
- the indifference of the outside world to a civil war
- the violation of human rights
- religious conflict
- the human spirit's will to survive

Are there any other themes which you feel are important in the play?

Use one of the above topics as the basis for an essay.

2   *When is a war over?*
     If there is no shooting any more
     or there is no more hatred?

                                                                    page 116

Working in small groups, prepare for and stage a debate on this question.

3   *Refugees are never welcome ...*
     Refugees don't exist.

                                                                    page 6

Djuka's heartfelt words make us think about what happens to people who have to leave their own country because of civil war – or perhaps because of a natural disaster such as drought or famine. Carry out some research into what has happened to Bosnian refugees as a result of the war. Extend your researches by collecting newspaper articles on refugees – in different parts of the world – currently in the news. Write up your findings, complete with photographs and any reliable statistics you can discover.

4 War of any kind has its horrors. Civil war – when people within one country fight each other – has a particular brutality. Look back though the play and make a note of any references to family members, former friends and neighbours turning against one another. What, according to the playwright, might cause people to turn against one another? Where do your sympathies lie?

5 Now research more widely in your library and current newspapers. Concentrating on the 1990s draw up a list of countries which have experienced civil war. Choose two countries and write an essay about their comparative experiences of civil war. Include maps and illustrations where appropriate.

6 On page 26 Djuka condemns the United Nations for not preventing mass murder. Read the following extracts from the Universal Declaration of Human Rights, adopted by the UN in 1948:

Article 1 All human beings are born free and equal in dignity and rights. They are endowed with reason and conscience and should act towards one another in a spirit of brotherhood.

Article 3 Everyone has the right to life, liberty and security of person.

Article 5 No one shall be subjected to torture or to cruel, inhuman or degrading treatment or punishment.

Article 9 No one shall be subjected to arbitrary arrest, detention or exile.

Article 13 Everyone has the right to freedom of movement and residence within the borders of each state. Everyone has the right to leave any country including his own, and to return to his country.

Article 14 Everyone has the right to seek and enjoy in other countries asylum from persecution.

Now compose a polite, strongly worded letter to your local Member of Parliament asking why such things as are described in *Mirad* are allowed to happen?

You could extend this assignment by reading the complete Declaration. Think about the aims of each Article as you read them. Then ask yourself which are being honoured or broken in our world today?

7 One of the questions that is always raised when a civil war breaks out is, what should other countries and/or the United Nations do? There are, of course, no easy answers. Read the following quotations from international politicians who favoured intervention.

- *While action is dangerous it is preferable to the alternative. That is the key lesson we have learned from Hitler, Chamberlain and the Holocaust.*

- *We must not shrink from the use of force if we are to have credibility. Humanitarian assistance must not become a substitute for curbing the aggression itself.*

- *Since this is now a war of aggression of state against state, we are committed under existing treaties to intervene. If we do not, we are violating our most important duties. Only a determined show of force can stop the murder in the former Yugoslavia.*

From your reading of **Mirad** do you think the playwright is in favour of other countries intervening in the war? In particular, study again the lines of Djuka and Fazila.

8 What are your own views on outside intervention, in relation to any civil war? Write a short essay on the subject. Then use your material to stage a debate on this topic.

9 Mirad's letters and diary lie at the heart of Part 1 of the play. Look back over the text again and remind yourself what information is conveyed by Mirad.

Then read the following extracts from **Zlata's Diary**. Subtitled **A Child's Life in Sarajevo** this real-life diary was written by an 11-year-old girl living in the city in the same period that Mirad writes. She addresses her diary to an imaginary friend, Mimmy.

140

Saturday, 18 April 1992

Dear Mimmy,

There's shooting, shells are falling. This really is WAR. Mummy and Daddy are worried, they sit up late at night, talking. They're wondering what to do, but it's hard to know. Whether to leave and split up, or stay here together. Keka wants to take me to Ohrid. Mummy can't make up her mind – she's constantly in tears. She tries to hide it from me, but I see everything. I see that things aren't good here. There's no peace. War has suddenly entered our town, our homes, our thoughts, our lives. It's terrible.

It's also terrible that Mummy has packed my suitcase.

Love,

Zlata

Monday, 20 April 1992

Dear Mimmy,

War is no joke. It destroys, kills, burns, separates, brings unhappiness. Terrible shells fell today on Bascarsija, the old town centre. Terrible explosions. We went down into the cellar, the cold, dark revolting cellar. And ours isn't all that safe, Mummy, Daddy and I just stood there, holding on to each other in a corner which looked safe. Standing there in the dark, in the warmth of my parents' arms I thought about leaving Sarajevo. Everybody is thinking about it, and so am I. I couldn't bear to go alone, to leave behind Mummy and Daddy, Grandma and Grandad. And going with just Mummy isn't any good either. The best would be for all three of us to go. But Daddy can't? So I've decided we should stay here together. Tomorrow I'll tell Keka that you have to be brave and stay with those you love and those who love you. I can't leave my parents and I don't like the other idea of leaving my father behind alone either.

Your Zlata

Thursday, 7 May 1992

Dear Mimmy,

I was almost positive the war would stop, but today ... Today a shell fell on the park in front of my house, the park where I used to play with my girl-friends. A lot of people were hurt. From what I hear Jaca, Jaca's mother, Selma, Nina, our neighbour Dado and who knows how many other people who happened to be there were wounded. Dado, Jaca and her mother have come home from hospital, Selma lost a kidney but I don't know how she is, because she's still in hospital. AND NINA IS DEAD. A piece of shrapnel lodged in her brain and she died. She was such a sweet, nice little girl. We went to kindergarten together, and we used to play together in the park. Is it possible I'll never see Nina again? Nina, an innocent eleven-year-old little girl – the victim of a stupid war. I feel sad. I cry and wonder why? She didn't do anything. A disgusting war has destroyed a young child's life. Nina, I'll always remember you as a wonderful little girl.

Love, Mimmy,

Zlata

Wednesday, 27 May 1992

Dear Mimmy,

SLAUGHTER! MASSACRE! HOR-
ROR! CRIME! BLOOD! SCREAMS!
TEARS! DESPAIR!

That's what Vaso Miskin Street
looks like today. Two shells exploded
in the street and one in the market.
Mummy was near by at the time. She
ran to Grandma's and Grandad's.
Daddy and I were beside ourselves
because she hadn't come home. I
saw some of it on TV but I still can't
believe what I actually saw. It's unbe-
lievable. I've got a lump in my throat
and a knot in my tummy. HORRI-
BLE. They're taking the wounded to
the hospital. It's a madhouse. We
kept going to the window hoping to
see Mummy, but she wasn't back.
They released a list of the dead and
wounded. Daddy and I were tearing
our hair out. We didn't know what
has happened to her. Was she alive?
At 16.00, Daddy decided to go and
check the hospital. He got dressed,
and I got ready to go to the Bobars',
so as not to stay at home alone. I
looked out of the window one more
time ... and I SAW MUMMY RUN-
NING ACROSS THE BRIDGE. As
she came into the house she started
shaking and crying. Through her
tears she told us how she had seen
dismembered bodies. All the neighbours came because they had been
afraid for her. Thank God, Mummy
is with us. Thank God.

A HORRIBLE DAY. UN-
FORGETTABLE. HORRIBLE!
HORRIBLE!

Your Zlata

Tuesday, 27 October 1992

Dear Mimmy,

There's talk at the Bobars that Maja
and Bojana might be going to
Austria. Is that possible? Will they go
and leave me too? I don't dare think
about it. They're not crazy about
the idea either. We'll see what happens. There's talk of another Jewish
convoy leaving Sarajevo.

Your Zlata

Thursday, 29 October 1992

Dear Mimmy,

Mummy and Auntie Ivanka (from
her office) have received grants to
specialize in Holland. They have letters of guarantee, and there's even
one for me. But Mummy can't
decide. If she accepts, she leaves
behind Daddy, her parents, her
brother. I think it's a hard decision
to make. One minute I thing – no,
I'm against it. But then I remember
the war, winter, hunger, my stolen
childhood and I feel like going.
Then I think of Daddy, Grandma
and Grandad, and I don't want to
go. It's hard to know what to do. I'm
really on edge, Mimmy, I can't write
any more.

Your Zlata

Monday, 2 November 1992

Dear Mimmy,

Mummy thought it over, talked to
Daddy, Grandma and Grandad, and
to me, and she's decided to go. The
reason for her decision is – ME.
What's happening in Sarajevo is
already too much for me, and the
coming winter will make it even
harder. All right. But ... well, I suppose it's better for me to go. I really
can't stand it here any more. I talked
to Auntie Ivanka today and she told
me that this war is hardest on the
children, and that the children
should be got out of the city. Daddy
will manage, maybe he'll even get to
come with us.

Ciao!

Zlata

Friday, 6 November 1992

Dear Mimmy,

Mummy and Auntie Ivanka are trying to get all their papers and signa-
tures. It's now certain that Maja and
Bojana will be going to Austria. They
signed up for the Jewish convoy.
Maybe we'll leave on that convoy
too.

Zlata

What do Zlata's diary entries and Mirad's letters and diary have in common? Compare their attitudes to war and the events around them? Do you think they see things differently or the same as the adults around them?

10 Read the following lines by Pastor Martin Niemöller:

First they came for the Jews
and I did not speak out
because I was not a Jew.

Then they came for the communists
and I did not speak out
because I was not a communist.

Then they came for the trade unionists
and I did not speak out
because I was not a trade unionist.

Then they came for me —
and there was no one left
to speak out for me.

At the end of the play Verica says to Mirad:

Write the story of this war.
So that nobody will forget
how terrible
and how senseless it was.

Do human beings learn the lessons of war? Why is it important for writers, artists, photographers, journalists to cover the subject of war? Discuss these questions in groups; write up your conclusions.

Study questions

Many of the activities you have already completed will help you to answer the following questions. Before you begin to write, consider these points about essay writing:

- Think about what the question is asking. Underline key words or phrases.
- Use each part of the question to 'brainstorm' ideas and references to the play which you think are relevant to the answer.
- Decide on the order in which you are going to tackle the parts of the question.
- Write a first draft of your essay.
- Redraft as many times as you need, ensuring all the time that:
  - each paragraph answers the question;
  - you have an opening and closing paragraph which is clear and linked to the question set;
  - you have checked for spelling and other grammatical errors.

1 Do you find the play overall to be optimistic or pessimistic? Answer with close reference to the text.

2 'I have hope that what's happened to us will not happen to them' (page 13). Discuss whether you think a play such as **Mirad, A Boy from Bosnia** has the power to change people's opinions.

3 A good play should educate and entertain at the same time. Does **Mirad** succeed?

4 This is a play which you need to see on stage in order to appreciate its full power? Discuss this statement.

5 'I was shaken to read a good play on a subject that threatens to overpower the writer' (page 136). Do you consider that the subject matter dominates at the expense of good drama? Give your reasons.

6 The play would have been more effective if the playwright had introduced more characters onto the stage. Comment on this view.

Suggestions for further reading

Non-fiction

Bosnia, A Short History by Noel Malcolm

This skilfully researched book offers the best available background history to a country where the great religions and great powers of Europe have overlapped and combined.

Never Again?

This leaflet published by the UK Friends of Bosnia gives brief and useful information about the Bosnian war in the 1990s.

Fiction

Journey to Jo'burg by Beverley Naidoo

A forceful, short novel which has echoes of ***Mirad*** in its tracing of two young children's challenging journey in search of their mother; South-African setting.

Sumitra's Story by Rukshana Smith

A compelling novel which traces the events in the life of a young Asian girl who has come to Britain because her family had to leave their native Uganda.

Zlata's Diary by Zlata Filipovic

The extraordinarily mature diary of an 11-year-old caught up in the Bosnian capital Sarajevo during the same civil war that Mirad experiences.

The Diary of Anne Frank

The celebrated diary of a young Jewish girl's experiences during the Second World War (1939–45).

STUDY PROGRAMME

Mischling, Second Degree by Ilse Koehn
In common with Anne Frank, Ilse was a young Jewish girl who lived under the reign of Nazi terror – in Berlin and various evacuation camps. Her autobiography makes for powerful reading.

Children of the Dust by Louise Lawrence
A novel which hauntingly charts lead character Sarah's fight against the horrors of nuclear war.

Drama

The Jail Diary of Albie Sachs by David Edgar
Set in the period of apartheid in South Africa, this is the story of a young lawyer, imprisoned for his beliefs, who seeks to hold out against his interrogators.

The Silver Tassie by Sean O'Casey
Set in the period of the First World War (1914–18), this moving and beautiful play tells the story of a war casualty returning to his family in Ireland.

Wider reading assignments

1 Read a few scenes from one of the above plays about war. How does the style and content of the drama compare with *Mirad*?

2 Read and compare the style and content of Anne Frank's and Zlata's diaries.

3 What similar ideas and issues relating to the treatment of refugees can you find in *Mirad* and *Sumitra's Story*?

4 *In a war everything can happen he says.*
   Even a miracle.

page 8

146

Write an essay on this subject, referring to *Mirad* and the experiences of Zlata, Ilse Koehn and Anne Frank.

5. 'There is no such person as a war survivor'. Discuss the meaning of this statement with close reference to *Mirad* and any two of the above titles. Use quotations from the texts in your answer.

Other titles in the Longman Literature series are listed on page ii.

Longman Group Limited,
Longman House, Burnt Mill, Harlow,
Essex CM20 2JE, England
and Associated Companies throughout the world.

© Verlag der Autoren, D-Frankfurt am Main 1994
© English translation Marian Buijs NL – Heemstede 1994

The right of Ad de Bont as author and the right of Marian Buijs as translator of *Mirad, a Boy from Bosnia* has been asserted by them in accordance with the Copyright, Design and Patents Act 1988.

This educational edition © Longman Group Limited 1995

First published 1995

Editorial material set in 10/12 point Gill Sans Light
Produced by Longman Singapore Publishers (Pte) Ltd
Printed in Singapore

ISBN 0 582 24949 X

Acknowledgements

We are grateful to the following for permission to reproduc copyright material: British Red Cross Society for an extract from th article 'British Red Cross: Aid to former Yugoslavia' in the programm of the Oxford Playhouse presentation of Mirad: A Boy from Bosn (1994); Minority Rights Group for the poem ' First They Came f the Jews..' by Pastor Martin Niemoller; Penguin Books Ltd f extracts from Zlata's Diary by Zlata Filipović, translated by Christir Pribichevich-Zorić (Viking, 1994). Copyright © Fixot et Éditior Robert Laffont, 1993, 1994, 1995; John Retallack, Artistic Directc Oxford Stage Company for extracts from his Introduction in th programme of the Oxford Playhouse presentation of Mirad, A B from Bosnia (1994).

With acknowledgement to John Retallack and Ian Lanyon for the charts on pages 131 and 133.

Cover illustration by Jason Walker

The publisher's policy is to use paper manufactured from sustainab forests.

Consultants: Geoff Barton and Jackie Head